BUTTERFLIES

of

NORTHAMPTONSHIRE

To Bryan
with best wishes
Douglas Goddard

Douglas Goddard & Andy Wyldes

ACKNOWLEDGMENTS

A publication of this kind would not be possible without the many observers, too numerous to mention individually, whose records of sightings and anecdotes have contributed towards building up the overall picture of the status of our species, past and present.

Others with greater specialist knowledge in Butterfly Conservation have provided very valuable insights into our rarer butterflies. Matthew Oates in his inimitable, inspirational style has helped us to unlock the many secrets of the world of the Purple Emperor. The Wood White looked on the verge of extinction until the timely intervention of Dr Stephen Jeffcoate, Dr Jenny Joy and Dr Martin Warren. Monitoring over a long period by Andy Patmore, Wildlife Ranger South Northants District, and his local knowledge provided valuable information in setting up the Recovery Plan for this species. For insights into the management of the Black Hairstreak, we must again thank Andy Patmore, as well as Dick Smith, warden of Glapthorn Cow Pastures, and Ioan Thomas.

Conservation now plays an increasing part in the work of our local branch. At Fermyn Woods Country Park, the hospitality and support for our winter work parties from Hilary Monk, Pete Burdett and Phillippa Croucher has been much appreciated and they have readily taken on board our suggestions for management of the Country Park to benefit butterflies. Similarly, Jane Pearman, Reserves Manager for the Northants Wildlife Trust, has welcomed and supported our input into the management and monitoring of the Twywell Hills and Dales site. We have also worked on the Sywell Country Park Butterfly Garden by kind permission of Geoff Simon and Rachel Axford.

Photographs have very kindly been provided by Matthew Oates (Purple Emperor and Comma aberrations), Jack Seward ('BB' and his Purple Emperors) Hilary Monk (Camberwell Beauty), Ioan Thomas (Chequered Skipper), Bob Bullock (Silver-studded Blue), David Newland (Black-veined White, Large Blue and Large Tortoiseshell) and information for distribution maps by Dr Jim Asher and Richard Fox, National Surveys Managers, Butterfly Conservation.

The staff at Northampton Public Library were most helpful in providing access to the Natural History Society Journals in their possession, to allow an historical perspective to be included.

Martin Izzard proved invaluable in securing a printer for this book and advice on its final production. Thanks are due to Adrienne Leeder for checking the general text and Peter Tebbutt the scientific names and butterfly content.

This publication has been funded by the Beds & Northants Branch of Butterfly Conservation and all proceeds will be used to support its work in the area.

A group of Butterfly Conservation volunteers at Fermyn Woods Country Park carrying out valuable conservation work

CONTENTS

This is the first book ever to be written about the butterflies of Northamptonshire and it makes a special contribution to the Natural History of this county. The authors are admirably suited to do this. Douglas Goddard has been County Recorder for the last twenty-five years and writes from his long experience in a very readable way. Andy Wyldes was introduced to the idea of photographing butterflies when he was a boy in the 1970s and he and Douglas have taken most of the photographs in their book. These pictures are really action shots of the butterflies showing details which could be easily overlooked, like the difference in the tips of the antennae of the Small and Essex Skippers. Each species is illustrated by several photos and different stages of the life cycle are also shown.

To some extent British Butterflies have been saved by photography. Many early records do not give details of locality because of anxiety about collectors. The extinction of the Large Blue near Oundle in the C19 has been attributed to collectors, though it could not have survived in the 1940s when the rough grassy field with ant hills near Barnwell Wold was converted into arable. One of the sources which Douglas Goddard has used is the 1910 edition of a History of British Butterflies by the Rev. F. O. Morris. The book describes a fifty foot long net made so that the Purple Emperor could be captured – though the plate shows the specimen caught in Rev. William Bree's hat! Collectors were rarely satisfied with one specimen for their cabinet and there was a busy trade in rare species. When I was first shown the Purple Emperor in Fermyn Woods twenty-five years ago I was almost sworn to secrecy about the site. Now there is a web-site (noted in this book) with lots of details and encouragement for those who want to see this astonishing insect. Butterfly hunting has come of age!

But I do not agree with Douglas Goddard when he writes in his introduction that the book is not a scientific work. Certainly it is not a dry and dusty tome those words might suggest, but the information contained provides a great deal towards understanding the ecology of each of the species. Collectors may no longer be a menace but changes in land management and changes in climate may be serious threats. Ignorance and complacency present the greatest risks and this wonderful book will do much to avert those dangers. We need lots of observers prepared to submit written records to provide the foundation of a better understanding of the ecology of each species. Moreover we need lots of volunteers to keep the habitat right and examples of work like this are illustrated in this book.

British butterflies are still vulnerable. A marvellous book like this will do much to secure their future.

Ioan Thomas

Photographs of the Northants Chequered Skipper are few and far between. The picture and note (to the left) was once hanging on the notice board of Oundle School in 1958. The picture was taken by one of the pupils. A record by the Chaplain (Phillip Edwards) in 1956 tells us, "The last two seasons have been particularly frustrating......The only kind which never fails is the Chequered Skipper. Sometimes we forget how rare an insect this is because we see it in every woodland path and glade nearby. Many collectors are without them. If they want them they must come to woods within 15 miles of Oundle to get them."

CHEQUERED SKIPPER

A butterfly found commonly in woods round Oundle. It is on the wing from the end of April until early June. It is restricted to woods in Northamptonshire.

Northamptonshire has always held a special place in the pursuit of butterflies. In the nineteenth century Victorian collectors came from far and wide to track down the Large Blue, Chequered Skipper and Black-veined White and the county was well worked by a number of local clergymen. 53 species were listed in *The Victoria County History* in 1901. We can find many references to our butterflies in the writings of eminent local writers and naturalists such as John Clare, Dame Miriam Rothschild and 'BB' (Denys Watkins-Pitchford) The latter cherished a lifelong passion for re-introducing the Purple Emperor to his native county. Today, a new army of visitors from the length and breadth of the country, laden with cameras instead of collecting nets, descends on Fermyn Wood where the largest English colony of this butterfly now exists. Glapthorn Cow Pastures is equally a place of pilgrimage for the elusive Black Hairstreak and Salcey Forest a national target for the Wood White.

The earliest accounts of the distribution of our local butterflies are contained within the first journals of the Northamptonshire Natural History Society and the Oundle School Natural History Society, plus the Kettering and District Natural History Society records – further details are contained in the Further Reading section. These give an impression of the abundance of species, much greater than now, with details of localities where the key species had been collected. Not until a survey of 1976-81, co-ordinated by Ian Flinders, my predecessor as county recorder, do we have an attempt to plot the distribution of species on a geographical basis. This was done in 10 km. squares, based on sightings of adults only with no records of the early stages. This provided a useful starting point for modern study, and the information was incorporated into national publications. The computer age has enabled recording to be done to a larger scale of distribution and annual records are now submitted electronically to the national database of Butterfly Conservation. Maps for the period 2006-2010 are included in the species' texts.

This book aims to collate the historical information on individual species for the first time, as well as providing an up to date picture of their specific characteristics, distribution and conservation status in the county. It is not intended as a field guide, nor is it a scientific work, but I hope the descriptions and inclusion of the early stages will assist the beginner as well as inform the specialist. It is not a definitive account, but aimed as a stimulus and encouragement to a growing band of enthusiasts who venture out to see our local butterflies, enjoy them and provide records. Hopefully, as a result, more people will become interested enough to join Butterfly Conservation. There is also scope for others to unearth extra historical information and make amendments to any errors, the responsibility for which remains entirely with me.

Douglas Goddard   Northamptonshire Butterfly Recorder, 1986 to Present.

Distribution Maps

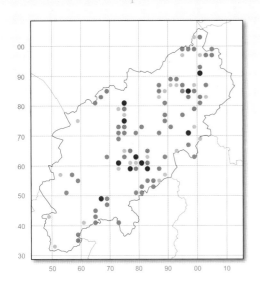

The distribution map for each species is taken from the national Butterfly Conservation database for 2006-2010 and covers the current geographical county of Northamptonshire. Vice county 32 consists of Northamptonshire and the Soke of Peterborough and is still used for recording biological data. A number of sites mentioned in the historical section such as Barnwell Wold, Helpston Heath and Castor Hanglands are in the vice county but are now part of Cambridgeshire.

Key to Distribution Maps

- 1 sighting
- 2-9 max seen
- 10+ max seen

The Beds and Northants Branch is one of 31 Butterfly Conservation branches in the United Kingdom. Set up in 1984/5, it has over 300 members locally. The aim of the society is to conserve and maintain butterfly and moth species within their natural habitats. The Branch produces a newsletter three times a year, providing up to date information for members and reports on the local species and conservation issues. It also runs a keenly contested annual photographic competition and during the summer holds several field trips in the area, on which to observe the butterfly species present.

Recording

Recording of the butterflies is carried out by branch members and the results provided to the national database, which forms part of a five-year cycle of reports on species trends. Only by recording regularly can declines and expansions of species be monitored and research and conservation measures undertaken. Members are kept informed of the latest sightings in the county on the branch website
www.bedsnorthants-butterflies.org.uk

Since 2009, members have participated in the Wider Countryside Butterfly Survey, involving the counting of common species in an allotted km. square in order to assess trends for butterflies outside nature reserves and other well-recorded sites.

One of the allotted squares for the WCBS near Slipton

Training day for participants in the Black Hairstreak survey 2007

Species of Conservation Concern

Northamptonshire has thirty-five species which are recorded annually. Of these, seven are BAP (Biodiversity Action Plan) species, of major conservation concern, for which action is a priority:

Grizzled Skipper Dingy Skipper	Found in mainly old limestone quarry sites in the county.
Wood White	Still present in most of our major south Northants woodlands, but declining.
White-letter Hairstreak	Breeds on Elm trees.
Small Blue	Confined to one small colony near Brackley, last recorded 2008, possibly extinct.
White Admiral	Present in most of our larger woods.
Small Heath	Locally distributed, declining.

The county is also of major importance for the Black Hairstreak, which is only found in part of the East Midlands, and the Purple Emperor, of which Fermyn Wood in north Northants holds the largest colony in Britain. The Branch produced a leaflet on the Black Hairstreak for landowners and other interested parties, advising on its conservation, following a survey with the Wildlife Trust in 2007. This followed a similar study of the Purple Emperor in 2004 and ongoing observation of this species is carried out as part of a national project.

Management of Key Sites

Butterfly Conservation works closely with other organisations on sites where key species are present. During the winter months we carry out scrub clearance in order to ensure that the caterpillar foodplants of Dingy and Grizzled Skippers are able to thrive. In Northamptonshire this has been on the Wildlife Trust's site at Twywell Hills and Dales and at Fermyn Woods Country Park where new glades have also been created in the adjoining thicket for the Black Hairstreak. The Branch was instrumental in setting up the Butterfly Garden at Sywell Country Park, on which we have also carried out maintenance.

Scrub clearance at Fermyn Woods Country Park

Working on the butterfly garden at Sywell Country Park

A Lepidopteran Strategy for Woodlands has been set up by National Head Office to work with Forest Enterprise to conserve important species in this key habitat in the county. Of particular concern is the decline of the Wood White butterfly throughout the country. Northants used to be a major stronghold for this species and a Recovery Plan was launched to arrest its decline. A dossier of key sites was produced to identify sites for conservation.

Identifying Wood White habitat in Salcey Forest

Working to Bring Butterflies to the Wider Public

Members of our branch provide talks to Wildlife Groups, Gardening Clubs and other organisations on butterflies, in return for a donation towards our conservation work. Guided walks outside our branch programme also take place. We put on displays and sell goods at local events. We have recently provided funds for the provision of an information board on butterflies which has been erected near the Visitors' Centre at Fermyn Woods Country Park where we hold an annual 'Butterfly Day'.

Information board at Fermyn Woods Country Park

Our sales stand at Fermyn Woods CP Butterfly Day

As more and more natural habitats are destroyed by housing developments, intensive farming and road building, gardens have become increasingly important as staging posts for butterflies between nature reserves and the wider countryside. They afford an opportunity for everyone to watch butterflies at close quarters and derive enjoyment from them.

For the past twenty years, Butterfly Conservation has conducted a National Garden Butterfly Survey, co-ordinated by Margaret Vickery. Some twenty species are recorded regularly in this habitat in England:

Most commonly Recorded Species	Less Commonly Recorded Species	Least Commonly Recorded Species
Peacock	Painted Lady	Common Blue
Large White	Speckled Wood	Ringlet
Small White	Comma	Small Copper
Red Admiral	Orange-tip	Small Skipper
Small Tortoiseshell	Meadow Brown	Large Skipper
	Gatekeeper	Wall Brown
	Green-veined White	
	Brimstone	
	Holly Blue	

Nectar Sources

The first course of action for attracting butterflies into the garden is to plant a range of nectar plants which will flower throughout the seasons. The one shrub which everyone knows as 'The Butterfly Bush' is the Buddleia and most gardens will boast at least one. It is particularly associated with the aristocrats of the butterfly world, the Nymphalids such as Peacock, Small Tortoiseshell, Comma, Red Admiral and Painted Lady. The White species, including the Brimstone, also find it attractive. Buddleias are best pruned vigorously in February and March. If several are planted in the same garden, it is a good idea to cut them down in stages to extend the flowering season.

There is a direct link between availability of nectar and visiting butterflies; gardens with thirty or more flowering plants in sunny positions will attract the highest numbers of species. Plants should be massed together with as little bare ground as possible and kept well watered in times of drought. A range of flowers should be in bloom throughout spring and summer. Wild flowers are best if space is available, which is rarely the case in urban settings, but butterflies find a range of cultivated plants very much to their taste. A good selection for spring would be Aubretia, Primrose, Honesty and Sweet Rocket, Sweet William and Wallflower. In summer, Buddleia, Chrysanthemum, Ice Plant (*Sedum spectabile*), Verbena bonariensis, Lavender, Marjoram, Michaelmas Daisy, Hebe, Red Valerian and Candytuft would prove a beneficial selection. It goes without saying that insecticides should not be used. Paths and mown lawns should be kept to a minimum. Shelter to the north and east is essential; hedges are better than walls.

Left: Painted Ladies feeding on Buddleia
Below: Wild flower area in a garden. Seeds for this sort of project can readily be purchased on the internet

Caterpillar Food Plants

Butterflies are very specific in the choice of plants on which to lay their eggs and since each species will only use a single or limited number of foodplants, it is difficult to provide for more than a few.

Perhaps the most common breeding species in the garden environment are the Large and Small Whites. They are well-known for the caterpillars' devouring of cabbages in the vegetable garden, but will just as readily lay their eggs on Nasturtiums and even Stocks. In a good season these plants will be laden with eggs and caterpillars of both species.

Orange-tip caterpillars will feed on Honesty and Green-veined Whites on Aubretia, both plants thereby serving a dual purpose, since they are good early-season nectar sources. The same is true of Holly – adult Holly Blues feed on the blossoms and the caterpillars on the developing buds. This species also takes advantage of a number of other berry-bearing shrubs, such as Pyracantha, Portugal Laurel and Alder Buckthorn, while the foodplant of its second brood is Ivy. Buckthorn is a foodplant of the Brimstone and many butterfly enthusiasts plant it especially to attract this species.

The common Stinging Nettle is used by a wide range of the Vanessid butterflies, the Red Admiral, Small Tortoiseshell, Peacock and Comma, so if space provides, it is well worth leaving a patch in a wild part of the garden. They need to be in a large clump in a sunny position but even then they may not always be used. Cutting in mid-summer encourages fresh growth for the broods of these butterflies later in the year. Areas of longer meadow grasses with Bird's-foot-trefoil and Garlic Mustard growing under a hedge will provide for the common Browns, the Common Blue and Orange-tip.

Above: Batches of Large White eggs on Nasturtium leaf
Below: Holly Blue caterpillar feeding on Holly berries. Note the ants in attendance, a common occurrence within the Blue family

The Value of Ivy

A clump of Ivy over a garden wall, garage or shed, or growing in the hedge is of immense value for butterflies. It flowers very late in the year when few other nectar sources are available and its strong scent proves to be a lure for numerous Red Admirals, Small Tortoiseshells and Commas, as well as Painted Ladies if they are still around. The Holly Blue lays its eggs among the developing buds. The Brimstone will choose a thick mass of Ivy in which to hibernate as an adult butterfly and the plant creates valuable shelter from the elements.

Hibernation in the adult stage is also a key component in the life cycle of the Comma, Small Tortoiseshell, Peacock and Red Admiral. They may find their way into a shed, garage or outhouse for this purpose. it is also worth leaving heaps of vegetation, dead leaves and piles of sticks or logs and dead flower stems as possible over-wintering sites for other insects. The need to build up reserves during the autumn may also be provided for by windfalls from any fruit trees present. Red Admirals and Commas often become intoxicated by long spells of feeding on the fermenting fruit.

Above: A Brimstone sheltering underneath an Ivy leaf, the veins of the butterfy matching it perfectly
Below: A Red Admiral nectaring on Ivy flowers in Cogenhoe churchyard

A leaflet "Gardening for Butterflies" is available from Butterfly Conservation and more information can be found on the national website www.butterfly-conservation.org

9

A ride in Bearshank Wood

Northamptonshire was once much more extensively wooded than it is now. In the Middle Ages, three main hunting forests were established. Rockingham Forest stretched from Northampton to Stamford, with an average breadth of 7-8 miles. Salcey comprised 1100 acres of coppices around Salcey Lawn, and Whittlewood occupied 600 acres. Today, a mere 5% of the land area of the county is forested. Only a fifth of this is ancient woodland, containing Ash, Field Maple, Hazel and Oak. The rest is plantation of either broad-leaved trees or conifers.

Management of the woods in the past consisted of coppicing. The regular cutting of the trees created a sequence of open glades followed by the re-growth of coppice stools. In the glades, light reached the woodland floor, the soil warmed up early and spring flowers, especially violets, flourished along with the butterflies. The abandonment of coppicing in the 1950s together with the mature growth of conifer plantations led to the decline and eventual loss of the Chequered Skipper, Duke of Burgundy and the Fritillary species in particular. Spraying of insecticides to eradicate Oak Tortrix moths further contributed to extinctions.

By the 1980s, the bushy edges of access rides had attained optimum conditions for the Wood White to thrive, even in the conifer plantations, but by the start of this century these were becoming too shaded again for this butterfly, which began to decline markedly in the county. At the same time, growth of Honeysuckle in sheltered conditions helped the White Admiral to re-colonise all of our larger woodlands. Sallow regenerates readily on the clay soils of the East Midlands and the Purple Emperor has enjoyed a welcome expansion of its range. The initiative to remove conifers from our forests to re-create native broadleaf woodland has benefited the Wood White again. The Silver-washed Fritillary has re-colonised since 2007, part of a natural expansion as a result of climate change. More open conditions will only help its resurgence.

Important relics of the three ancient forests still survive. Fermyn Woods, part of the old Rockingham Forest, is particularly rich in woodland butterfly species. Purple, White-letter and Black Hairstreaks, Purple Emperor, White Admiral and Silver-washed Fritillary all occur within this complex. Geddington Chase also has a colony of the Purple Emperor, while the Silver-washed Fritillary can now be found in good numbers in Wakerley and

Fineshade Woods. White-letter Hairstreaks can be seen around a number of elms in Fermyn and Fineshade, while the smaller woods around Glapthorn are good breeding grounds for the Black Hairstreak. Salcey Forest and Yardley Chase remain nationally important for the Wood White and all of the above species are still present, though some are hard to find. The Purple Emperor was recorded again in Yardley Chase (2009 -2011) and Salcey (2011). The remnants of the old Whittlewood Forest, comprising Wicken, Hazelborough and Bucknell, also hold strong Wood White populations, Purple Emperor and Silver-washed Fritillary have made a comeback, though Black Hairstreak is absent and White-letter Hairstreak rare.

Recent operations have improved our woodlands for butterflies, opening up rides and creating new glades and clearings, but the habitat still remains threatened. In the present economic climate, cuts in Forestry Commission budgets are likely to curtail future management and conservation work. Some woods, such as Wicken, have been sold to private ownership and others may well follow in the future.. Butterfly Conservation will face an important challenge to ensure that effective management plans are drawn up for the continued survival of our key arboreal species.

Left: Ride widening in Harry's Park Wood
Above: Prime Purple Emperor territory along Stephen Oak Riding
Below: Sudborough Woods in spring
All three pictures part of the Fermyn Woods Complex

11

There are 60,000 acres of grassland in Northamptonshire, though much of this has been intensively farmed, re-seeded and fertilised, reducing the wildlife value. Grasslands can be broadly categorised as calcareous, neutral or acid.

Calcareous Grasslands are found principally on the oolitic limestone of the Jurassic ridge which crosses the county and on thin, porous soils, frequently rocky and lime-rich. These limestone grasslands provide some of our richest habitat for butterflies. The best known are managed by the Wildlife Trust and are described in greater detail in the section on key sites. Quarrying at Collyweston created an undulating landscape which could not be ploughed and the bare rock and spoil heaps became colonised by a diverse flora. At Bradlaugh Fields, a former golf course, are good areas of unimproved, semi-natural limestone grassland. Old Sulehay is another former quarry site within the ancient Rockingham Forest. At Twywell Hills and Dales ironstone extraction formed a deep gullet with exposed limestone banks. The Whitestones area here was formed from limestone spoil. Specialist butterflies of limestone grassland are Dingy and Grizzled Skippers, Green Hairstreak and Small Heath, most localised in Northamptonshire and threatened nationally. These sites have also provided ideal habitat for the expansion of the Marbled White.

Neutral Grasslands, the soils of which are neither acid nor alkaline, are widespread in the county and comprise flood meadows, old ridge and furrow, usually on boulder clay, and hay meadows. Grass in flood plains contains caterpillar foodplants for a number of species: Lady's Smock for Orange-tip and Green-veined White, Docks for Small Coppers, nettles for the Vanessid species and grasses for Browns and Skippers.

Above right: Twywell Hills & Dales, one of the best butterfly sites in the county
Below: Old Sulehay which has good numbers of Grizzled and Dingy Skippers

Acid Grasslands are limited in Northamptonshire and are restricted to the acid, free-draining soils overlying liassic sands in the west of the county. Heath occurs where these have a deep layer of humus but only exists now in small areas. Relatively few species of butterflies are found in acid grasslands compared with the other types.

Loss of damper grasslands through drainage in the past would have contributed to the demise of species such as the Marsh and Small Pearl-bordered Fritillary. The greatest threat to our remaining habitat today comes from the ever-increasing pressure for new building development.

Insecticide spray and drift can damage the quality of a site, while lack of management soon leads to the development of scrub and coarser plants which choke out the wild flowers. This has led to a decline in many species in localities which are not under protection and where resources are not available to ensure their survival in the desired quantity. Overgrazing by rabbits and stock can also degrade sites and the local branch of Butterfly Conservation works closely with the Wildlife Trust at Twywell Hills and Dales, monitoring the butterfly populations in the light of scrub clearance by volunteers and winter grazing by cattle and sheep.

Above: Collyweston is still a good place to find Green Hairstreaks in the spring

Below: Short vegetation and bare ground is achieved with livestock grazing, providing ideal habitat for Dingy Skippers

Livestock are used to help keep scrub down, this group of cows helping out at one of the scrub clearing days at Twywell Hills and Dales!

Gardens and Parks

Gardens are most people's first point of contact with butterflies. They are assuming increasing importance as more residents become interested in attracting and conserving their wildlife. A good range of nectar plants will lure many common species while Holly and Ivy provide caterpillar foodplants for the Holly Blue. Ivy is used by Brimstones to hibernate and as a late summer nectar plant for Nymphalid species, which can also be encouraged to breed by nurturing a nettle patch. Planting Alder Buckthorn can entice Brimstones to breed and the Speckled Wood has become an increasingly common visitor to gardens in Northampton.

Large gardens with formal flower beds, such as those at Delapre Abbey Northampton,will reward a visit in late summer as will the Butterfly Garden at Sywell Country Park. Large areas of manicured lawns dominate many of our open spaces but parks in Northampton such as Abington and Eastfield are particularly good places to find Holly Blues and Speckled Woods, while at Wicksteed Park in Kettering, Purple and White-letter Hairstreaks were discovered in the arboretum in 2011.

Above: The gardens at Delapre Abbey, Northampton
Right: The old railway line at Brackmills, Northampton, a good place to find Orange-tips in the spring
Below: Abington Park, Northampton, excellent for Holly Blues

Hedgerows and Roadside Verges

At first glance, driving along the county's roads, the butterfly habitat may not be obvious. In spring Brimstones and Orange-tips can be seen easily from a distance as they patrol their territories. Stop to take a closer view and the Gatekeepers, Meadow Browns and Ringlets will be found later in the summer, along with a range of others if the grass is not too long and wild flowers are allowed to flourish. Adjacent untrimmed hedgerows with Holly and Ivy and Alder Buckthorn afford breeding grounds for the Holly Blue and Brimstone. Broad field margins and headlands with a sheltered hedgerow alongside can attract a wide range of butterflies, while wayside oaks and elms are worth perusing for Purple and White-letter Hairstreaks. Roadside verges can act as wildlife corridors connecting sites. The construction of bypasses at Daventry and Bozeat assisted greatly in the dispersal and countywide expansion of the Marbled White.

Disused Railway Lines and Airfields

The construction of railway cuttings and embankments with the associated soil disturbance created flower-rich grassland on poor soils. When many of the lines were closed in the 1960s, this, along with the warm ballast on the track bed, created ideal conditions for butterflies. On the railway line between Helmdon and Radstone in the 1980s over thirty species were recorded, including Dingy and Grizzled Skippers, Wood White, Green Hairstreak, Dark Green Fritillary and Marbled White. The two Skippers were also to be found on a number of other tracks with several colonies of the Grizzled Skipper existing on the Brampton Valley Way towards Market Harborough. However, as the lines passed into private hands, without the incentives or resources to manage them, they gradually became more overgrown leading to a decline in the butterflies. Today the disused lines at Farthinghoe and Woodford Halse survive as nature reserves, with good colonies of Marbled Whites. Even these are threatened by proposed plans to build a High-speed Rail Link through south Northants. Wood Whites can still be found on the county boundary on the line adjacent to Yardley Chase, the site of the largest colony in Britain in the 1980s.

Disused airfields offer large areas of open space, often with much bare ground and very sparse vegetation, providing an ideal habitat for the Grizzled and Dingy Skipper, Small Copper, Common Blue, Brown Argus and Small Heath in particular. Many of these have succumbed to the plough, but good habitat still exists at Polebrook where Dingy and Grizzled Skippers still fly and Black Hairstreak has been recorded among the scrub. Spanhoe airfield, adjacent to Wakerley Wood, once held large numbers of Dingy and Grizzled Skippers and a healthy population of Green Hairstreak but the site has gradually reverted to scrub leaving a much diminished area of suitable habitat, though these were all recorded here in small numbers in 2011, along with Brown Argus and Small Heath. Harrington, a site renowned for bird migrations, has a good population of Small Heath.

Harrington airfield

Spanhoe airfield, near Wakerley Wood

Polebrook airfield. Black Hairstreaks have been recorded here again after an absence of many years

Churchyards

Churchyards and cemeteries may form an oasis of open space within an urban setting or in areas of intensive farmland. Here a range of conditions exists to provide for the needs of butterflies. The grassland, though often mown, may contain a host of wild flowers. The walls and gravestones retain heat and there may be hedgerows, trees and shrubs which create shelter and nettles, Holly, Ivy and Bramble which provide for all stages of the life cycles, including hibernating quarters.

Typical churchyard butterflies are the Holly Blue, Brimstone, Speckled Wood, as well as the common Whites, Nymphalids and Browns. Large numbers of Red Admirals with some Commas and Small Tortoiseshells, can often be seen around the Ivy blossom on warm days in early autumn in the grounds of Cogenhoe, Little and Great Billing churches and in the old cemetery at Finedon. Newton Bromswold and Stoke Doyle are excellent examples of 'God's Acre' which are managed specifically to preserve their flora.

A Red Admiral suns itself on a gravestone in Cogenhoe churchyard

Finedon's old cemetery, good for Holly Blues and Speckled Woods in springtime

Quarries, Gravel Pits and Reservoirs

Quarries have already been mentioned as important grassland sites. Fortunately, the best of these have been designated as nature reserves, though some, such as sites adjacent to Weekley Hall Wood, have suffered from the encroachment of scrub. Others, like Irchester and Brigstock, have become Country Parks. The huge gullet at Irchester has become overgrown but the site at Brigstock, now Fermyn Woods Country Park, is important for Dingy and Grizzled Skippers and Green Hairstreak. Such a setting cannot be grazed so volunteers from Butterfly Conservation and other groups undertake winter scrub clearance here.

A series of gravel pits exists along the Nene Valley between Northampton and Thrapston, comprising Wildlife Trust nature reserves at Storton's Pit, Northampton, Summer Leys near Great Doddington, Ditchford Lakes, Higham Ferrers Pits and Thrapston Gravel Pits. The Stanwick Lakes site is run by the Rockingham Forest Trust. These localities offer much wet grassland around the margins of the rivers, ponds and lakes for Orange-tips, Green-veined Whites, Small Tortoiseshells and Large Skippers. In the early stages of reclamation the sparse vegetation allowed species such as Common Blue, Small Copper and Brown Argus and in the case of Thrapston, Grizzled Skipper to colonise readily. These sites are a regular haunt of the Clouded Yellow when it graces the county from the continent. Similar conditions for butterflies prevail around the reservoirs of the county, such as Pitsford, Hollowell and Sywell.

Above: Weekley Hall Wood quarry was once a stronghold of the Wall Brown

Storton's Gravel Pits, Northampton, a Wildlife Trust reserve

Below: Part of the Gullet section at Twywell Hills & Dales, the yellow carpets of flowers being Common Bird's-foot-trefoil, caterpillar food plant of Dingy Skippers, Green Hairsteaks, and Common Blues

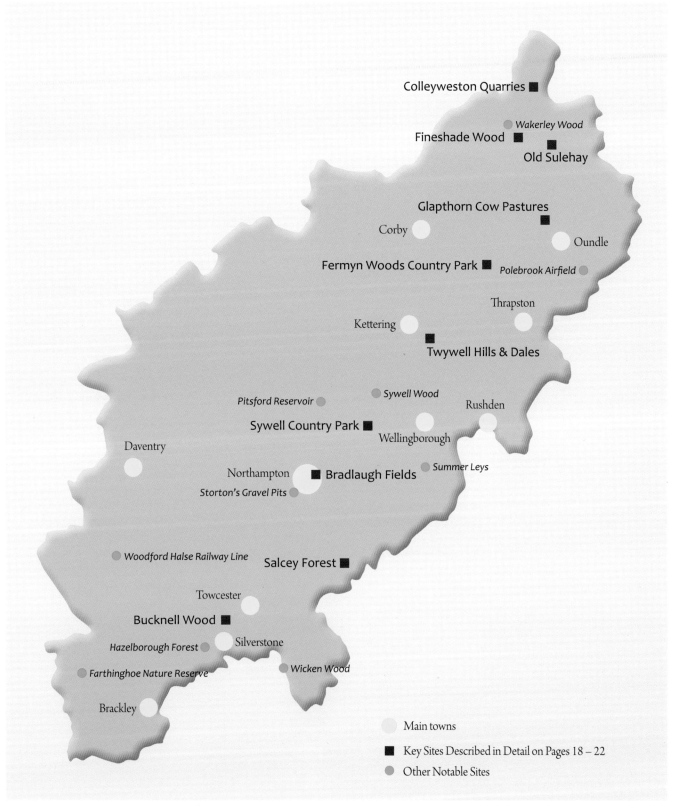

Colleyweston Quarries
Wakerley Wood
Fineshade Wood
Old Sulehay
Glapthorn Cow Pastures
Corby
Oundle
Fermyn Woods Country Park
Polebrook Airfield
Thrapston
Kettering
Twywell Hills & Dales
Sywell Wood
Pitsford Reservoir
Rushden
Sywell Country Park
Wellingborough
Daventry
Northampton
Bradlaugh Fields
Summer Leys
Storton's Gravel Pits
Woodford Halse Railway Line
Salcey Forest
Towcester
Bucknell Wood
Hazelborough Forest
Silverstone
Wicken Wood
Farthinghoe Nature Reserve
Brackley

○ Main towns

■ Key Sites Described in Detail on Pages 18 – 22

● Other Notable Sites

Above is a selection of sites in Northamptonshire, which at the appropriate times of year will enable visitors to see nearly all of the species present in the county. These have been chosen for their public accessibility and to give a geographical spread across the area. Details of other localities of key importance and flight periods are given in the accounts of the individual species which follow.

BRADLAUGH FIELDS, NORTHAMPTON

Close to Northampton, within the larger Bradlaugh Fields Park, three meadows are managed by the Wildlife Trust on part of a former Golf Course. The reserve consists of unimproved, semi-natural limestone grassland and fragments of ancient hedgerow. Especially in the part known as Hills and Hollows, next to the Kettering Road, an array of wild flowers can be found providing nectar and caterpillar foodplants. As well as common butterflies, large numbers of the grassland species are present, especially the Browns and Skippers, including Essex Skipper. Good quantities of Common Blues and Brown Argus fly here and it is one of the best sites in the county for the Small Copper and Small Heath. Immigrant Clouded Yellows are often recorded and a colony of Marbled Whites has become established.

BUCKNELL WOOD

Part of the old Whittlewood Forest, this semi-natural ancient woodland, managed by the Forestry Commission, is 4 miles south-east of Towcester, between Silverstone and Abthorpe. Although the site consists mainly of mixed conifers, these are being reduced to encourage the native broadleaved woodland. It is one of the strongholds of the Wood White and around the oaks Purple Hairstreaks are sometimes abundant, with good numbers of White Admirals in the sheltered glades and rides. In recent years the Purple Emperor and Silver-washed Fritillary have made a welcome comeback and the White-letter Hairstreak was recorded in 2011. Many common species can also be seen enjoying the flowers on the sides of the more open rides. It is worth combining a visit with nearby Hazelborough Wood where Wood White, Purple Hairstreak, White Admiral, Silver-washed Fritillary and Purple Emperor can also be found and where White-letter Hairstreak has been recorded in the past.

COLLYWESTON QUARRIES

Five miles from Stamford, between Easton-on-the Hill and Collyweston on the A43, these quarries were once the source of Collyweston slate, a limestone used to roof many traditional stone buildings in the area. The grassland, a Wildlife Trust reserve, now hosts a variety of wildflowers, some rare in the county. Among them are Dyer's Greenweed, Common Rockrose and Bird's-foot-trefoil, used as caterpillar foodplants by the Green Hairstreak, Brown Argus, Dingy Skipper and Common Blue respectively. All of these are to be found here along with a strong colony of Marbled Whites, which can be seen in July nectaring on the many flowers of Greater Knapweed, Scabious and Clustered Bellflower. The undulating ground provides shelter for a range of other common butterflies, notably Small Heath and Small Copper.

FERMYN WOODS COUNTRY PARK

Situated to the east of Brigstock, just off the A6116, this Country Park with its mixture of disused quarries and mature woodland, provides a range of habitats. Successive visits throughout the season may be rewarded with sightings of nearly all of the Northamptonshire species. Spring is the time to visit the limestone grassland near the visitor centre. The undulating terrain creates natural suntraps and shelter from the wind, and the south-facing banks generate warmth. Here the Green Hairstreak is common around the Hawthorn bushes, and good numbers of Grizzled and Dingy Skippers are present along with Brown Argus and Small Copper. In summer the grass is alive with Skippers, Meadow Browns, Ringlets and Gatekeepers and the occasional Marbled White. The adjacent thicket is the home of the Black Hairstreak in June, and July is the time to join the throng of countrywide visitors to see the Purple Emperor, White Admiral, Silver-washed Fritillary and Purple and White-letter Hairstreaks, all of which are in good numbers in Cherry Lap and Lady Wood.

The Beds and Northants Branch, along with other volunteer groups, works very closely with the park rangers to clear scrub in the quarry area for the grassland species and create new glades in the thicket for the Black Hairstreak.

FINESHADE WOOD

Part of the old Rockingham Forest alongside the A43, 8 miles from Stamford, Fineshade contains rich semi-natural woodland along with areas of conifers that are gradually being restored to native broadleaf forest under the 'Ancient Woodland Project'. In the more open rides, many common butterfly species can be seen and Purple and White-letter Hairstreak, White Admiral and Silver-washed Fritillary are frequently encountered. Near the old railway line Grizzled Skippers may be recorded, and in 2010 the Black Hairstreak was found.

Across the road Wakerley Wood is also worth a visit. Silver-washed Fritillaries were flying in good numbers here in 2010 and 2011 and Purple Hairstreaks and White Admirals are present.

GLAPTHORN COW PASTURES

Two and a half miles from Oundle, Glapthorn Cow Pastures is a Wildlife Trust Reserve and SSSI, consisting of Blackthorn scrub and mature woodland. It is managed by a group of volunteers who maintain the rides and glades within the Blackthorn for the rare Black Hairstreak. During its short flight period in June, visitors from all over the country descend on this site where the butterfly can be seen at close quarters nectaring on Dewberry, an early-flowering species of bramble which grows here. A range of common species are also present within the reserve and during July it is worth looking in the northern part of the wood, consisting of Ash and Oak, where White Admiral, Purple Hairstreak and Silver-washed Fritillary may be seen.

OLD SULEHAY

One of the Wildlife Trust's largest reserves in Northamptonshire near the village of Yarwell, Old Sulehay forms a fragment of the ancient Rockingham Forest in the far north of the county, 7 miles from Stamford. As well as woodland, it consists of old limestone quarries with a mixture of scrub, grassland and bare ground. White Admirals and Purple Hairstreaks may be found among the trees while the more open areas of Stonepit Close favour the localised Dingy and Grizzled Skipper and Green Hairstreak, along with Common Blues, Brown Argus and Small Coppers. Among the abundant Browns a strong colony of Small Heath flies and the Marbled White has colonised recently. It is worth combining a visit with the adjacent Ring Haw where similar grassland butterflies can be found. Black Hairstreak has also been recorded there.

SALCEY FOREST

This remnant of the medieval hunting forest, managed by the Forestry Commission, lies to the east of Hartwell between Northampton and Newport Pagnell. Much of the ancient oak woodland remains and the conifers which had been planted there are gradually being removed. The Black Hairstreak, once found in a number of locations here, has become very hard to find in recent years, but the rides still hold many of our woodland species. Of particular importance is the Wood White, seen in May and June on the flowers of Ragged Robin, Bush Vetch and Meadow Vetchling. In July White Admirals, Purple Hairstreaks and occasional White-letter Hairstreaks fly with the more common species. In recent years the Silver-washed Fritillary has made a comeback and a colony of Marbled Whites can be seen in the meadow near the M1 motorway. In 2011 the Purple Emperor was seen for the first time in half a century.

SYWELL COUNTRY PARK

This disused reservoir has a butterfly garden situated in one of the old filter beds adjacent to the south-facing bank of the dam. The garden was formally opened by the late Gordon Beningfield over twenty years ago, after preparatory work by Butterfly Conservation and the park rangers who continue to maintain it with local volunteers. The sunken site is a suntrap for much of the day and the range of flowers, including Buddleia, Michaelmas Daisies, Marjoram and Golden Rod, attracts good numbers of common species. September is perhaps the best month to visit when the Red Admirals, Commas, Small Tortoiseshells, Peacocks and Brimstones are feeding prior to their hibernation. They are joined by Gatekeepers, Holly Blues which breed on the profusion of Holly and Ivy around the car park, and especially the Small Copper. The dam also has a number of breeding grassland species.

TWYWELL HILLS AND DALES

This Wildlife Trust Reserve is managed with the Rockingham Forest Trust and is 5 miles from Kettering, just north of Junction 11 of the A14. The eastern part of the reserve comprises a deep gullet of steep banks exposed by the extraction of limestone. Across from the car park is the area known as Whitestones which was formed by limestone spoil. The latter, a mixture of scrub and flower-rich hollows, is an excellent area for Grizzled and Dingy Skippers, Green Hairstreaks, Small Coppers and Small Heaths in spring, followed by large numbers of Marbled Whites and Browns, and Skippers in late June and July. The Beds and Northants Branch of Butterfly Conservation carries out winter work parties to clear scrub and maintain the key species while a weekly transect count is conducted to monitor closely the population trends of all the butterflies present. The Gullet is less accessible but is worth visiting to find similar species. White-letter Hairstreaks did occur here until the elms succumbed to disease, though one was still seen in 2010.

NORTHAMPTONSHIRE'S CURRENT BUTTERFLY SPECIES

Species		Northants Status	National Status
Skippers	*Hesperidae*		
Small Skipper	*Thymelicus sylvestris*	Widespread	Common, expanding range
Essex Skipper	*Thymelicus lineola*	Under-recorded	Common SE, expanding NW
Large Skipper	*Ochlodes sylvanus*	Common	Common
Dingy Skipper	*Erynnis tages*	Uncommon	**BAP Priority Species**
Grizzled Skipper	*Pyrgus malvae*	Uncommon	**BAP Priority Species**
Whites	*Pieridae*		
Wood White	*Leptidea sinapis*	Declining woodland species	**BAP Priority Species**
Clouded Yellow	*Colias croceus*	Migrant, common some years	Annual migrant, especially SE
Brimstone	*Gonepteryx rhamni*	Common	Common
Large White	*Pieris brassicae*	Common	Common
Small White	*Pieris rapae*	Common	Common
Green-veined White	*Pieris napi*	Common	Common
Orange-tip	*Anthocharis cardamines*	Common	Common
Blues	*Lycenidae*		
Green Hairstreak	*Callophrys rubi*	Uncommon	Widely distributed, uncommon
Purple Hairstreak	*Favonius quercus*	Found in most larger woods	Widespread in oak woodland
White-letter Hairstreak	*Satyrium w-album*	Uncommon/under-recorded	**BAP Priority Species**
Black Hairstreak	*Satyrium pruni*	Uncommon	Restricted to East Midlands
Small Copper	*Lycaena phlaeas*	Widespread	Common
Small Blue	*Cupido minimus*	One small colony maybe extinct	**BAP Priority Species**
Brown Argus	*Aricia agestis*	Widespread	Common SE, expanding
Common Blue	*Polyommatus icarus*	Common	Common
Chalkhill Blue	*Polyommatus coridon*	Vagrant	Restricted southern downland
Holly Blue	*Celastrina argiolus*	Common, especially some years	Common
Nymphalids	*Nymphalidae*		
White Admiral	*Limenitis camilla*	Widespread in larger woods	**BAP Priority Species**
Purple Emperor	*Apatura iris*	Expanding in larger woods	S woodlands, expanding
Red Admiral	*Vanessa atalanta*	Common migrant, overwintering	Common migrant/resident
Painted Lady	*Vanessa cardui*	Migrant, common some years	Migrant, abundant some years
Small Tortoiseshell	*Aglais urticae*	Common, some recent decline	Common, some recent decline
Peacock	*Aglais io*	Common	Common, expanding
Camberwell Beauty	*Nymphalis antiopa*	Rare migrant	Rare migrant
Comma	*Polygonia c-album*	Widespread/common	Common, expanding
Dark Green Fritillary	*Argynnis aglaja*	Rare vagrant	Widely Distirbuted
Silver-washed Fritillary	*Argynnis paphia*	Recent expansion in woodlands	S,W woodland, expanding NE
Browns	*Nymphalidae Satyrinae*		
Speckled Wood	*Pararge aegeria*	Common	Common
Marbled White	*Melanargia galathea*	Widespread, often numerous	Common in south, expanding
Gatekeeper	*Pyronia tithonus*	Common	Common
Meadow Brown	*Maniola jurtina*	Common	Common
Ringlet	*Aphantopus hyperantus*	Common	Common
Small Heath	*Coenonympha pamphilus*	Uncommon	**BAP Priority Species**

Small Skipper *Thymelicus sylvestris*

The male (wingspan 30mm.) is recognised by the black curved line on the forewing, the sex-brand

The Small Skipper, not the smallest of the British Skipper butterflies, is very widespread throughout Northamptonshire. Like the Large Skipper, it is not often found in gardens unless a colony is nearby but vast numbers can build up on large areas of grassland. The species can be found in a variety of habitats where even a small patch of Yorkshire Fog, the favoured caterpillar foodplant, grows in tall clumps. Open grassland, old quarries, roadside verges and disused railway lines are all likely to harbour good colonies but on damper woodland rides, riverbanks and marshy areas, it is likely to be outnumbered by the Large Skipper. Numbers can vary considerably from year to year, depending on the weather during the emergence period.

The Small Skipper is unlikely to be confused with the Large Skipper on close inspection. It is a smaller species and lacks the mottled markings, being a plain golden-orange colour on both the upper and underside of its wings. The male is easily distinguishable from the female as there is a black curve, the sex-brand, on each forewing. This helps to distinguish it from the male of the very similar Essex Skipper which has a shorter, straighter black line. Both species are difficult to follow in their swift, busy flight. When seen at rest the orange or brown underside of the tips of the antennae can be seen; in the Essex Skipper, these are black. Such identification is best done in dull or cool weather when both can be easily found at rest, with wings closed, on grass stems or flower heads. Variation occurs occasionally in the ground colour, as in the pale aberration *pallida* recorded in Bucknell Wood in August 2005.

Local Distribution and Status

The Small Skipper is common throughout Northamptonshire where long meadow grasses are to be found in places such as grasslands, woodland rides, waste ground and man-made sites which have reverted to nature and even roadside verges. Its numbers have declined nationally on monitored sites over the past few years. Good locations to see it in the county are Bradlaugh Fields, Twywell Hills and Dales and along rides in our larger woods.

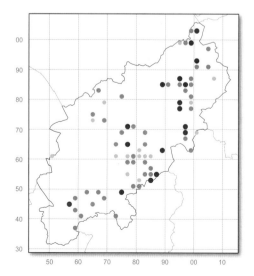

Below: Roosting on the top of grass stems away from spiders

This Skipper can be recognised by the orange underside tips of the antennae

Eggs are laid in a row inside the sheath of a grass stem

Two adults in typical pose with Six-spot Burnet moths

In most years the species appears towards the end of June, though warm weather advances emergence so that it may be seen two weeks earlier. The flight period is long, reaching a peak in mid-July with stragglers still being seen towards the end of August. Small Skippers have the characteristic zipping flight of the Skippers, remain within a specific area, and spend long periods of the day taking nectar from any flowers which may be available. Several can often be seen on one flower head, on the patches of thistles and clumps of Knapweed, Wild Marjoram and Ragwort which are such a feature of its grassy habitats. Bramble blossoms are also favoured in woods and hedgerows.

Life Cycle

Females lay eggs during July and August in rows of three to five inside the grass sheaths of Wood False Brome, Yorkshire Fog or Cocksfoot. The caterpillars, on hatching, spin tiny silk cocoons around themselves and remain in the sheath throughout the winter. They emerge in April to feed on the tender new growth of leaves. They then separate to eat singly creating a shelter in which to feed by spinning two leaves together. Pupation takes place in June at the base of grasses in a loose tent of leaves.

Since the food plant is a common grass species in all types of soil and this butterfly flourishes in a variety of habitats, the future of the Small Skipper in Northamptonshire is not seriously threatened. However, agricultural improvement, housing development and landfilling have inevitably brought about a reduction in the number of colonies.

Female perched on Kidney Vetch flower

	Jan	Feb	Mar	Apr	May	Jun	Jul	Aug	Sep	Oct	Nov	Dec
Egg												
Caterpillar												
Chrysalis												
Butterfly												

Essex Skipper *Thymelicus lineola*

Feeding adult (wingspan 27 mm.) showing the black tips to the underside of the antennae

Local Distribution and Status

The Essex Skipper was absent from the nineteenth century records as it had not been recognised as a species. Since then it has become well distributed throughout the county though not all observers take the trouble to distinguish it from the Small Skipper. Thus it is difficult to monitor its spread accurately. It was described as widely distributed around Oundle in 1937. Records for Castor Hanglands (1964) mention it as occasional but recorded every year. Ian Flinders' survey (1976-81) documented its increasing appearance in sites in the west of the county but considered it to be under-recorded. He reported a ratio of 1:10 to the Small Skipper at Wellingborough but given that the flight periods of the two species overlap and are not simultaneous, the accuracy of this count is difficult to authenticate.

The Essex Skipper is a species could not figure in the early records for Northamptonshire, since it was not distinguished as a species until 1889. It would be worth investigating at some length the nineteenth century collections which exist, to determine how many of the Small Skippers in those are in fact misidentified Essex Skippers. The differences between the two almost identical species are described under the Small Skipper.

Both species frequent very similar locations and habitats and can often be found together on the same flower head of brambles, thistles, Ragwort or Knapweed. On dull days, or in cool conditions, both species rest with heads facing upwards and are relatively easy to inspect closely and identify accurately. Most observers understandably tend to record in warm, sunny weather, when both Essex and Small Skippers are very active, so the former is probably under-recorded. It is likely to be found throughout the county as in recent years it has spread nationally.

Typical resting pose on a grass stem

Life Cycle

The life cycle differs somewhat from that of the Small Skipper. The Essex Skipper hibernates as a fully developed caterpillar within the egg. With the protection of a robust shell it is able to survive winter flooding. Eggs are laid in July and August in the sheaths of a variety of grasses, including Cocksfoot and Creeping Soft-grass, but not Yorkshire Fog, the usual choice of the Small Skipper. Upon hatching in April, the caterpillar spins two edges of a tender spring grass blade, to form a feeding tube, in true Skipper fashion. The caterpillar's head is yellowish with three brown lines; that of the Small Skipper is pale green. The chrysalis stage lasts about three weeks. The flight period begins about a week later than that of the Small Skipper, from mid-July, lasting well into August, though is not as prolonged.

Nationally the Essex Skipper is by no means confined to East Anglia and is extending its range gradually throughout southern England. It may be that it has been spread by the transportation of grass containing the early stages but as more observers become familiar with it so more colonies are discovered. It is well worth looking for in any locality wherever there is a good growth of grass and variety of nectar plants, particularly on a warm summer's evening when it will roost communally and be settled enough to allow identification.

In terms of conservation, the species is not threatened and the same comments apply to both the Small and Essex Skipper, though much more needs to be done in studying both species when roosting to determine its status compared with the Small Skipper and its precise distribution in the county.

A mating pair

The undersides of the antennae are black

On the forewing the male has a shorter black sex-brand than the Small Skipper

	Jan	Feb	Mar	Apr	May	Jun	Jul	Aug	Sep	Oct	Nov	Dec
Egg												
Caterpillar												
Chrysalis												
Butterfly												

Large Skipper *Ochlodes sylvanus*

Male (wingspan 33mm.)

The Large Skipper is easily recognised by its golden appearance and the mottled pattern on its wings. This is particularly apparent when it is at rest with wings closed. It is noticeably larger than the other two 'golden' Skippers, the Small and Essex. The male has a distinctive black scent-band which distinguishes it from the slightly larger female on which the mottled pattern on the wings is also more marked. Only the Silver-spotted Skipper can be mistaken for this species but it is not present in our area. The species is very territorial and will return close to the same spot when disturbed like the Small and Essex Skippers.. It has a characteristic way of holding its wings when feeding or resting with forewings and hindwings held apart, the former at 45 degrees to the latter. At rest it will eventually close them above its body like most butterflies.

When the weather in spring is warm, it can appear in the last week in May but emergence time can vary considerably. Normally, the first males are on the wing at the end of the first week in June. They emerge a few days before the females and the peak flight period is at the end of the month. The single brood lasts until mid-August but by this time the wings are very worn and tattered, although there seems to be a staggered emergence. Very unusually it was recorded remarkably late in 2007, on 2nd September.

Colonies are usually small and the butterfly does not wander far from its origins. Males are similar to those of the Speckled Wood in that they will defend their sunny patch in a hedgerow or woodland clearing against fellow Large Skippers and other insects while making dashing sorties to locate females. These begin from the leaves of low-growing shrubs which serve as launch pads. Adults nectar throughout the day on a wide range of flowers. Late in the evening the species may be found in groups, basking on branches higher up on a sheltered bush, absorbing the last rays of the sun before roosting for the night.

Local Distribution and Status

The Large Skipper is a widespread butterfly in Northamptonshire to be found wherever clumps of coarse grasses grow -hedgerows, roadsides, waste ground, woodland rides and clearings. It is usually numerous where found. Agricultural intensification and general tidying operations have led to a diminishing number of colonies of this butterfly but it has always been common in our area and there is no reason why it should not remain so.

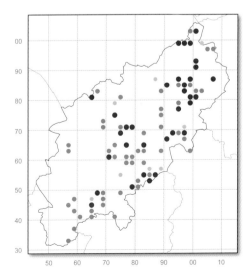

Female

Life Cycle

Cocksfoot is the most common foodplant and is most probably the one used in our area. Indeed, quite a thriving colony in a small patch of grassland in a school grounds was eliminated when the mowers encroached an extra metre into its edges. The eggs are laid on the underside of a leaf blade through June and July and the caterpillar creates a tube from the leaf, binding it with silk. It lives inside this tube nibbling the edges of the leaf. The Large Skipper caterpillar has a comb-like device which enables it to flick its droppings well away, to a distance of up to a metre so that its presence is not betrayed. Hibernation occurs after the first moult during September when it fastens together several blades of grass with silk, providing a shelter until the following March. The blue-green caterpillar with a black head then resumes feeding and moults twice more before pupating in May inside a cocoon within a tent created by several grass stems.

Mating pair – the difference between male (below) and female (above) can be seen clearly

Above and bottom right: The mottled pattern shows on the underside

Male showing black scent-brand on forewing

	Jan	Feb	Mar	Apr	May	Jun	Jul	Aug	Sep	Oct	Nov	Dec
Egg												
Caterpillar												
Chrysalis												
Butterfly												

Dingy Skipper *Erynnis tages*

Adult (wingspan 29mm.)

Local Distribution and Status

In Northants, the places for the Dingy Skipper are quite widespread. In the south-west of the county several colonies used to be found on disused railway lines. In north Northants, an abandoned airfield harboured a large colony but though the species was still present there in 2011, the site has gradually reverted to scrub and it will soon disappear from here. Disused quarries around Kettering at present hold the largest concentrations, far more than the maximum of 10+ recorded in Ian Flinders' survey of 1976-81. The 1976 drought may well have reduced sightings during this particular period.

The Dingy Skipper occupies very similar habitats to the Grizzled Skipper and is on the wing at the same time. It is a springtime species to be found in abandoned railway cuttings, disused quarries and airfields in Northamptonshire. On most sites it flies in company with the Green Hairstreak, with which it shares the same foodplant, Bird's-foot-trefoil. It fares best where the ground is frequently disturbed by rabbit activity, land slip or human actions so is not as widespread as the Grizzled Skipper in our area. The latter seems to be able to survive more easily as the natural succession of vegetation develops.

In flight the butterfly is rapid and difficult to identify, being a brown blur, and bearing some resemblance to day-flying Latticed Heath moths and the Burnet Companion. When fresh it has an intricate pattern of grey and brown on the wings which belies its popular name. However, the wing scales soon wear away to give it its drab and dingy appearance.

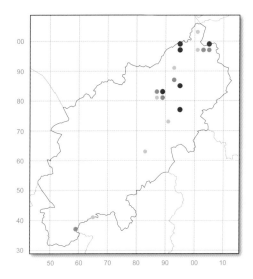

Roosting on a dead Knapweed head

Life Cycle

This species emerges in early May in most years or late April in an exceptionally warm spring. In 2011 it was first recorded on 20th April. The sexes are very similar. It is fond of basking on bare ground in between short flights, usually low over the terrain. In bright, sunny weather, the butterfly rests with wings outstretched but in duller conditions it assumes a moth-like roosting position, with wings draped over a flower head - Knapweed and Teasel seed heads are favourite perches and afford a particularly good camouflage. In dull weather, when it is too cold to fly, roosting adults of both Dingy and Grizzled Skippers can be found at rest on these.

On most sites, colonies are generally small. The eggs are therefore not easy to find unless a female is spotted laying one. They are laid on Bird's-foot-trefoil on the tender young leaflets or in the groove where the stalk joins the leaf. The caterpillar constructs a tent of leaflets spun together with silk. In August, when fully grown, its final shelter becomes its winter quarters until it pupates in April. In exceptional years one or two may emerge in August to form a partial second brood but this is most unusual in our area.

A succession of dry summers in the 1990s also led to a decline in numbers towards the end of the decade. This, coupled with the rise in the rabbit population which destroys essential ground flora, led to its virtual disappearance from one of its largest colonies in Northants, at Twywell Gullet, perhaps emphasising what a tenuous hold this species has in this area. There has been a recovery here and it can be found in good numbers at the present time, particularly in the Whitestones area. Other good localities are the old quarry areas of Fermyn Woods Country Park and Old Sulehay. In adjoining counties such as Lincolnshire it has become very scarce. In the early years of the last century it was very common in Northamptonshire, particularly in woods, a habitat from which it has now all but disappeared. Apart from a single specimen in 1992, at a well-known release spot, the last sighting in Salcey Forest, for example, was in 1986. There have been occasional records from Yardley Chase and in Wakerley Wood. It was recorded in Hazelborough in 2010 and Sywell Wood in 2011.

There have been reports of new sites for the Dingy Skipper as the number of recorders has increased but this is a species whose continued presence needs to be carefully monitored, and management work undertaken to clear the growth of vegetation which eliminates the foodplant. The largest threat to its present status, as with the Green Hairstreak, is the potential of its favoured habitats for landfilling and 'improvement'.

Fortunately several of its Northamptonshire sites are nature reserves or country parks. It can be very numerous in some years, but counts are generally small and it is important at least to maintain the butterfly's current sites. Members of the local branch of Butterfly Conservation have embarked on an annual programme of scrub clearance at Fermyn Woods Country Park and Twywell Hills and Dales in order to achieve this.

The egg is white when first laid, but then turns orange after a few days

Mating pair at Twywell, the female on the left

This species can often be found roosting in groups on dead flower heads

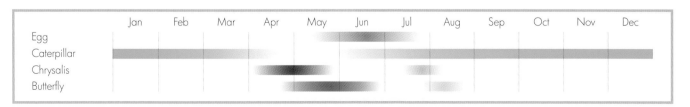

	Jan	Feb	Mar	Apr	May	Jun	Jul	Aug	Sep	Oct	Nov	Dec
Egg												
Caterpillar												
Chrysalis												
Butterfly												

Grizzled Skipper *Pyrgus malvae*

Adult (wingspan 27mm.)

Local Distribution and Status

The best places today are the old quarry sites in the Kettering area and it can be found in good numbers at Twywell Hills and Dales, Fermyn Woods Country Park and also at Stonepit Quarry in Old Sulehay. In recent years, our local branch of Butterfly Conservation has begun to undertake scrub clearance at Fermyn and Twywell which has benefited this and other species. A large colony on an old disused airfield near Wakerley has almost disappeared as scrub has developed.

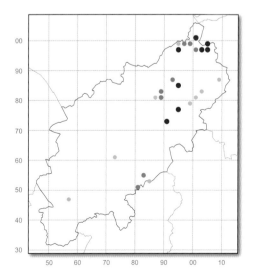

The Grizzled Skipper is one of our smallest spring butterflies, not an insect of the garden, but one which must be searched for. It is only seen by observers who venture into one of its wild domains – rough grassland, abandoned railway tracks, old quarry sites, disused airfields and wide woodland clearings. It is not easy to spot because of its small size and cryptic colouring when it settles on the ground. It also has a whirring flight which is difficult to follow. Furthermore, similarly patterned Latticed Heath moths abound in the same habitats. Nevertheless, it is an attractive little butterfly when it settles to be allow close examination.

The Grizzled Skipper usually basks with wings open in bright sunlight, often on bare ground among low vegetation. When seen closely it has a beautiful dark brown and white chequerboard pattern which extends to the fringes of the wings. Both sexes are similar though markings can vary from individual to individual. The underside is paler but the pattern is the same. Occasionally the white spots on the forewing may form a wide white central marking (aberration *taras*). The species rarely flies in dull and cloudy weather but in good colonies can be found quite easily roosting on dead seed heads, especially of Knapweed with which it blends superbly.

The butterfly can often be seen nectaring on a variety of plants and seems particularly fond of yellow flowers though it will also feed from the blossoms of Wild Strawberry. This is listed as a caterpillar foodplant and, indeed, is often abundant on many sites, but the eggs are more frequently laid on Creeping Cinquefoil or Tormentil in our area.

Life Cycle

Eggs are laid on the underside of leaves and are tiny, cream-coloured and bun-shaped. The caterpillar is a rather unattractive light brown with a black head. It protects itself by creating a shelter. Lying along the middle of a Cinquefoil leaflet, it spins the two edges together and eats the edges from the inside. It will move and construct fresh shelters as one source is consumed before pupating in a web of silk in which to over-winter at ground level.

There is normally one brood from early May to early June in most years though late April emergence takes place in warm springs (19th April in 2007). Prolonged cool weather can make the flight period very protracted. There are records of this in the past. For example in 1907, it was on the wing from 9th May to 11th July and in Castor Hanglands in 1961, the season lasted from 11th May to 16th July. Second brood individuals may be seen elsewhere in Britain but have not been recorded in Northamptonshire.

In 1907 the Grizzled Skipper was described as common, especially in woods and Yardley Chase and Sywell Wood were listed as well-known localities in the nineteenth century. Generally, however, it disappeared from this habitat as modern forestry plantation superseded the old, more open coppiced conditions. It is only just hanging on here, with recent records from Fineshade Wood and singles only from Yardley Chase in 2006 and 2007. The balance was redressed by the creation of new abodes which it happily colonised. The abandoned railway lines created corridors for dispersal where the foodplants thrived among the warm ballast. In the 1980s, these held very strong colonies, but the butterfly has now disappeared from a number of these as they have become more overgrown, at Charwelton, Farthinghoe and the Brampton Valley Way. It still exists at Helmdon and King's Cliffe station yards in small numbers.

In Ian Flinders' survey of 1976-81, the maximum number recorded was only 10+ at any site. This may be due to a reduction in sightings because of the drought of 1976. Similarly, a succession of dry summers in the 1990s led to a decline in numbers. This coincided with a rise in the rabbit population which destroyed essential ground flora. There have been reports of the species from new sites in the last decade as the number of recorders has increased and the Grizzled Skipper is still well distributed in the county. This is a species which needs to be carefully monitored, with management work undertaken to halt the degeneration of vegetation towards scrub which eliminates the foodplants. Fortunately Twywell, Fermyn and Old Sulehay are protected sites and the Beds and Northants branch is currently liaising with the appropriate bodies to ensure its survival. The largest threat to its status, as with the Green Hairstreak, lies in the potential of its favoured habitats for landfilling and 'improvement'.

Mating pair, female above, male below

Aberration Taras

At rest on Ribwort Plantain

Essential nectar is provided by small flowers

	Jan	Feb	Mar	Apr	May	Jun	Jul	Aug	Sep	Oct	Nov	Dec
Egg												
Caterpillar												
Chrysalis												
Butterfly												

Dingy and Grizzled Skippers
A Conservation Challenge

Butterflies are important biodiversity indicators. They are sensitive to the most subtle changes in their environment such the height of grass, the loss of foodplants for the caterpillars and nectar sources for the adults. This is no more apparent than in the case of the Dingy and Grizzled Skippers. Surveys of 1976 – 82 compared with 1995 –2004 indicated a decline in distribution of 48% in Britain of the Dingy Skipper and 49% of the Grizzled Skipper with both suffering steep long-term population declines. Such statistics matched the criteria for designating both of them Biodiversity Action Plan (BAP) Species, of conservation concern.

The Dingy Skipper thrives where Bird's-foot-trefoil grows in a sparse sward, often with patches of bare ground in a sunny, sheltered situation. The Grizzled Skipper requires Agrimony, Wild Strawberry, Creeping Cinquefoil and Tormentil growing in short vegetation (less than 5cm. high) and often next to bare ground, providing a warm microclimate for egg development. The adult butterflies need large quantities of nectar in spring or early summer, from daisies, Bugle, Bulbous Buttercup and Bird's-foot-trefoil. Strands of longer vegetation including seed heads from the previous year over 40 cm high are used for roosting. Maintaining all of the requirements for these two spring skippers constitutes a real conservation challenge.

Work at Twywell in early spring 2011 by members of the Butterfly Conservation Northants group to open up a south-facing bank from scrub to allow regeneration of Wild Strawberry plants, one of the Grizzled Skipper's main food plants

In 2008, numbers of the Dingy and Grizzled Skipper were lower than usual in the Whitestones area of Twywell Hills and Dales, an important site for both. Although this could be attributed partly to the poor weather, winter grazing by sheep and cattle had been introduced to the site and continued into spring. Although cattle break up the ground with their hooves, providing breeding pockets for the butterflies, they nibble the tender shoots of Bird's-foot-trefoil, the foodplant of the Dingy Skipper and the females avoid laying eggs on damaged plants. Sheep graze to a uniform height thus not providing the variety of sward which is suitable for both of these Skippers. They are also less likely to create areas of bare ground, favourite places on which to bask.

In some parts of the country Dingy and Grizzled Skippers have suffered extinction owing to overgrazing and the local branch of Butterfly Conservation expressed concern to the County Wildlife Trust which manages the Twywell site, over the level and timing of grazing and its impact on these vulnerable butterflies. A transect was set up to count all the butterflies in the Whitestones area in order to monitor trends in populations as a means of assessing the impact of scrub clearance, done by Butterfly Conservation and other groups, alongside grazing by stock.

The cleared bank with scrub left either side to help shelter the slope from winds

Management of the site consists of stock grazing by cattle and sheep until the end of March, a date which has become crucial as the Dingy and Grizzled Skippers consistently emerge before the end of April. Clearance work by Butterfly Conservation and other groups removes unwanted scrub by hand with a brushcutter being used to eliminate coarser grasses and create bare ground. Some scrub is left deliberately to ensure shelter and provide perches for the Green Hairstreak, a localised species in Northamptonshire but also a speciality of this site. Natural factors also have a positive impact on the Hills and Dales. There is some rabbit grazing and, in the gullies at the far end of Whitestones, landslip maintains sparse growth and patches of bare ground.

The same bank photographed in September 2011, Grizzled Skippers being recorded here in May on the transect walk

The Whitestones Transect

On a transect a set route is designated for counting the butterflies, usually divided into ten distinct sections. As the route is walked, the numbers for each species are recorded up to 2.5 metres either side of the path and 5 metres ahead. The count is conducted in the middle of the day, preferably in sunshine with little wind, or in temperatures above 17C. The transect is done weekly from the start of April until the end of September, a period of 26 weeks, at the end of which cumulative totals for each species as a whole and section by section can be obtained. Comparisons can be made year on year and short and long-term trends determined.

Trends for Key Species 2009 – 2011

Species	Total 2009	Total 2010	Total 2011
Dingy Skipper	71	125	143
Grizzled Skipper	30	56	98
Green Hairstreak	5	41	89
Brown Argus	30	64	87
Marbled White	298	331	93
Small Heath	69	186	284

It is clear that there has been an upward trend in the numbers of the species which need shorter vegetation like the Dingy and Grizzled Skippers. Two successive warm springs have helped the population to build. Large numbers of Green Hairstreaks were seen in 2011; the count of 49 on 1st May was the largest in the county for over two decades. Species such as the Brown Argus and Small Heath are double-brooded and in their late summer populations can be very numerous if they can breed well early in the year. The Small Heath is another UK BAP Species, and has shown a remarkable population rise from 2009 – 2011.

While the grazing and scrub clearance have established good habitat for the above, the numbers of Marbled Whites crashed on the transect in 2011. As well as the management regime, this could be attributed in part to the very dry spring which inhibited the growth of the grasses. The flight period can also be contracted in warm weather with numbers being confined to fewer weeks in the count. What it does illustrate is the need to maintain a site of varied grass heights and the difficulty of managing successfully for a range of species with widely different habitat requirements. Off the transect, in an area of long grass next to the main car park, Marbled Whites were still plentiful in 2011. Numbers of all butterflies fluctuate from year to year for various reasons, and only after a longer period of monitoring will truer population trends become apparent. Nonetheless, results from the first three years of the transect count have been encouraging.

Second Brood Dingy Skippers

Second brood Dingy Skippers are very rare, only occurring in warm southern sites in Britain after a hot summer. In Northamptonshire, before 2010, the only records were of singles at Charwelton and Old Sulehay in 1990 and 21st August 1999 at Weekley Hall Wood Quarry. In 2010, on the transect at Twywell a second brood individual, the first in this millennium, was sighted on 31st July, followed by a second on three occasions in late August. This was the first time more than one had been seen at a single site.

More remarkable sightings occurred at Twywell in 2011. A single butterfly was found on 5th August, followed by six on 14th and 15th August. This first multiple sighting of the second brood in the county was unprecedented and unexpected. In warm spring weather the Dingy Skipper emerged on 25th April in 2010 and on 20th April in 2011, allowing early egg-laying and completion of the life cycle. Climate change has brought much earlier first sightings of butterflies and extremes of temperature have led to unexpected appearance of unusual second broods. The exceptional spring conditions in 2010 ad 2011 brought these welcome sightings. Whether or not they become the norm in the future remains to be seen but, as our climate changes and average temperatures rise, such events should occur more often.

A second generation Dingy Skipper (one of six) found on 14th August 2011

Ideal habitat for egg-laying Grizzled and Dingy Skippers. Wild Strawberry and Bird's-foot-trefoil plants amongst others, overhang bare patches of earth, the exposed ground warming up in the sunshine, which raises the temperature around the plants a few degrees and helps create a microclimate in which the developing caterpillars will grow quickly

Wood White *Leptidea sinapis*

Female at rest (wingspan 42mm.)

Local Distribution and Status

The Silverstone area in South Northamptonshire is the present stronghold of this species, in Bucknell, Wicken and Hazelborough Woods. A good colony survives in Sywell Wood. Its other main sites, Salcey Forest and privately-owned Yardley Chase, possessed some of the best colonies in Britain in the 1980s. In 1985, the butterfly flew in hundreds along the rides of Salcey, In 2007/08, its numbers were very low for the third year in a row following successive years of poor weather during the flight period. Better spring weather since 2009 has seen an upsurge in numbers helped by some sympathetic management of existing rides and opening of new ones in these woods.

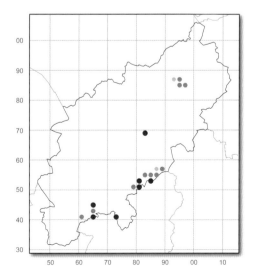

The delicate, deliberate flight of the dainty Wood White, reminiscent of falling flower petals, makes it easy to distinguish from other white butterflies. Dwarf specimens of Green-veined White flying weakly may cause confusion but at rest the oval wings of this species are distinctive, as is the habit of always resting with them closed. The male has clearly visible black tips to the forewings and orange tips to his antennae, with white blobs on them, while the slightly larger female has a small smudge on her wing tips with no white on the orange tips to her antennae.

The Wood White usually appears in mid to late May in our county with early May records in advanced seasons. In 2011 it was flying on 25th April. Emergence takes place over a long period with the peak period being in mid-June and a few still flying in mid-July. As with most butterflies, the population fluctuates from year to year with strong colonies supporting hundreds of butterflies in a good year. The species is at the northern edge of its range in Northamptonshire so a second brood is unusual, except in years when its early emergence is succeeded by a hot summer. Even then, only a few appear. They are smaller than those of the first brood and the black wing tips on the male are more intense and slightly reduced.

In hot, dry conditions the males can be seen in ditches in woodland rides, drinking from the water's edge to take up mineral salts. Flight of this species is generally at a low level and the Wood White will feed from a variety of flowers. Ragged Robin, Greater Bird's-foot-trefoil, Bugle and vetches are particular favourites. It will rest as soon as the sun goes in, but does so quite conspicuously, and can be spotted in the dullest conditions hanging from a leaf or perched on thistledown, vetches, Bugle or Bluebells, having the appearance of a white petal.

Male on Greater stitchwort

Life Cycle

The courtship of the Wood White is well worth watching. The male will perch opposite a female, uncoil his proboscis and wave his antennae back and forth. This usually happens in close proximity to the plants used for egg-laying. Females can often be seen depositing eggs on Meadow Vetchling, Greater Bird's-foot-trefoil or Tufted Vetch. The pale cream, bottle-shaped egg is large for a butterfly of this size and, with a little practice, can be spotted on large clumps of the foodplant, growing at the sides of rides in sunny, sheltered conditions. It is laid on the tender shoots towards the tips. The caterpillars' camouflage makes them difficult to find, though birds will discover them. The beautifully marked chrysalis is even more elusive. This is the stage in which this species spends the winter.

At the start of the twentieth century, the Wood White was absent from Northamptonshire. *The Victoria County History* for the county stated that it had been common over much of its range but in 1908 it had not been seen 'for quite 20 years.' In June of that year Mr Rothschild succeeded in capturing a male in the county. The danger in collecting rare species is perhaps implicit in the reference that it was 'not desirable to specify the exact locality.' The reason for its absence was the abandonment of coppicing at that time. By the 1950s commercial conifer plantations had provided ideal habitat again and the butterfly had reached the status of 'common in most woods around Northampton.'

There are two main areas for the Wood White in the county. One is centred on the woods in the south of the county, in the old Whittlewood Forest, where good numbers were seen in Bucknell, Hazelborough and Wicken Woods in 2011. It disappeared from Whistley Wood, formerly a strong site, in 2007. The other main area for the butterfly is in Salcey Forest and the many woods which make up the private Compton Estate in Yardley Chase. Beyond these is a good population in Sywell Wood and the edge of Hardwick Wood. Occasional Wood Whites are also seen in the Fermyn Wood complex. There were also colonies in the 1980s in disused railway cuttings where the foodplant occurs and where habitat mimics that of woodland rides but there have been no records from these in recent years, apart from Yardley Chase where the old line is adjacent to the woods. Such habitat needs continued removal of encroaching scrub for the butterfly to survive. The species sometimes strays from known colonies and singles have appeared at Pitsford Reservoir and Finedon Country Park in the past but normally the species has weak powers of dispersal.

The Wood White can survive adequately in conifer plantations providing its foodplants can grow in suitable conditions and rides of sufficient width are maintained. Clearance of areas within its woodlands will maintain its numbers for a while but these can quickly become overgrown and too shaded though the Wood White can survive in up to 50% shade. Northamptonshire's woodlands are a key area in Britain for the species making its conservation locally of paramount importance. The upward trend in populations over the last three seasons is cause for optimism but with the economic climate reducing the budget of the Forestry Commission and cutbacks in conservation work in our woodlands the habitat could quickly become unsuitable again. The sale of woods into private hands, as has already happened with Wicken Wood, also poses a potential threat to its survival.

The beginning of an elaborate courtship, male on the right

A female egg-laying on Meadow Vetchling

At rest on a Common Spotted Orchid

	Jan	Feb	Mar	Apr	May	Jun	Jul	Aug	Sep	Oct	Nov	Dec
Egg												
Caterpillar												
Chrysalis												
Butterfly												

THE CHANGING FORTUNES OF THE WOOD WHITE

'Several thousand (Wood Whites) emerge each year in Salcey Forest near Northampton adding immense charm to an ancient woodland that has been hideously disfigured by conifers' (*The Butterflies of Britain and Ireland* – Jeremy Thomas and Richard Lewington, 1st edition 1991)

In 2007 the Wood White, once such an abundant species, was giving major cause for concern. Records for that year, after three successive poor summers, showed only single-figure returns. This was not a low point which could be attributed solely to the weather. Transect counts dating back to 1987 carried out by Andy Patmore in colonies in six Forestry Commission Woodland blocks, highlighted a worrying long-term decline. The species is subject to cycles of population peaks and troughs but with each successive cycle since that date the peaks had become progressively lower and the troughs deeper.

In 2008, spearheaded by Dr Stephen Jeffcoate and Jenny Joy (Butterfly Conservation Regional Officer West Midlands), the National Wood White Recovery Plan was launched nationally by Butterfly Conservation. A National Sites Dossier was produced in 2010 (*Butterfly Conservation report S10-16*). In 2009, all major sites across the country were visited in spring to evaluate the habitat, and during the flight period to observe the butterfly and its behaviour. Douglas Goddard and Andy Patmore guided Stephen round key sites in the county. On June 23rd representatives of Butterfly Conservation, local and national including Dr Martin Warren, the Forestry Commission and Tony Richardson, the Conservation Officer for the Compton Estate, met in Salcey Forest and Yardley Chase. Dr Martin Warren had conducted an intensive survey of the population in Yardley Chase in the 1980s, when it was regarded as having the finest colony in Britain along the disused railway line. Several changes to the traditional management were suggested:

➤ To introduce more variety into the ride management, to achieve some ground disturbance where possible and to encourage vetch growth, by more aggressive mowing and stacking timber on the sides of rides away from traditional loading bays.

➤ To explore options for varying the ride cutting. At present each edge is cut back to the ditch in alternate years, which destroys over-wintering pupae on the mown side.. It is preferable to cut stretches, rather than the whole ride length, moving to a three-year rotation and leaving some patches uncut.

➤ In areas where vetches are sparse, the amount of foodplant may increase if a flail mower is used to rotavate the ride surface instead of swipe-mowing.

➤ On the woodland side of the ride ditches, scallops should be created through the small shrubs to act as "hot spots" for the Wood White.

Counts of Wood Whites showed an increase in 2009 as a result of improved weather during the flight period. The above measures were applied to selected areas of Salcey, Yardley Chase and Hazelborough and at the same time new rides and clearings were being created within the Northamptonshire woodlands as part of an initiative for the restoration of ancient woodland. 2010 had warmer than average weather from the end of May until the end of July. This led to an amazing upturn in the fortunes of the butterfly. In 2010 the Wood White was seen from 13th May, a relatively early date, and egg-laying was observed before the end of the month. Maximum counts in June included 39 in Wicken Wood, 29 in Hazelborough South Block, 40 in Salcey Forest and 33 in Yardley Chase.

In 2011 the warmest spring on record brought the emergence of the Wood White in April for the first time in the county on 25th. New nectar sources included Bluebells and Wild Ransoms. Numbers built quickly in Salcey Forest during May: 10 on 1st, 47 on 9th, 90 on 19th. Other counts were 43 in Bucknell Wood and 36 in Wicken (20th), 57 in Yardley Chase (21st) and 30+ in Hazelborough on 11th June, representing the best year since 1990 for this species. Near to Sywell Wood the species was found in newly cleared ditches next to Hardwick Wood, an old site, the inside of which is now very overgrown and along the bridleway to the south-east.

Dr. Martin Warren in Yardley Chase

Douglas Goddard and Dr. Stephen Jeffcoate in Salcey Forest

A Second Brood

Second brood Wood Whites are rare in Northamptonshire. They only occur after an early emergence date and/or a warmer than average summer. Records prior to 2010 consisted of few butterflies: 2 in 1989, on 24th August, the latest recorded date here, a singleton in 1990, 3 in 1992 (all Salcey) and 5 in 2003 in two parts of Yardley Chase. In 2010, following a sighting in Yardley Chase on 22nd July, 16 were found in Sywell Wood and 2 in Wicken (31st), 7 in Hazelborough south block and 4 in Bucknell Wood (3rd August). Egg-laying was seen in Sywell, Hazelborough and Bucknell, the first time this had been observed in the second brood in the county.

2011 brought an even greater second brood recorded in nine woods across the county range of the species, i.e. Sywell, Hazelborough south block, Salcey, Bucknell Wood and five sections of Yardley Chase. The cumulative total was at least 38 butterflies between 22nd July and 19th August constituting a sizeable emergence. The second brood is much more short-lived than the first. The males are very small and the dark mark on the apex of the forewing is blacker and less extensive. The markings on the apex of the wing are also smaller on the female.

In other parts of the country, for example Herefordshire and Warwickshire, the Wood White has become double-brooded as a result of climate change (in the south and south-west this has always been the norm). Prevailing conditions in 2010/11 have been exceptional and it remains to be seen whether the species has started to have a second brood on a permanent basis here. Females were seen laying in more open situations in 2011 on Greater Bird's-foot-trefoil and Tufted Vetch as well as the usual Meadow Vetchling, and the work of the Forestry Commission in creating new rides and clearing glades and intersections has created warmer situations for egg-laying and promoting quicker development of the caterpillars.

While these trends are positive indicators for the future of the Wood White, with intervention coming at a crucial time coinciding with a peak in the population cycle, there is no room for complacency. Only with continued appropriate management of our woods will populations thrive at sustainable levels.

Above: Second brood Wood Whites. Lower picture shows Meadow Vetchling, the preferred plant for egg-laying in Northants

Below: Sywell Wood has produced second brood Wood Whites in 2010 & 2011.

Clouded Yellow *Colias croceus*

Male (wingspan 57mm.)

Local Distribution and Status

The Clouded Yellow's appearance in Northamptonshire on a more regular basis is most welcome. Although it may be encountered almost anywhere, it appears to favour the restored gravel pits of the Nene Valley, being seen regularly at Summer Leys, Stanwick Lakes and Storton's Gravel Pits in Northampton. It has also been recorded on several occasions at Twywell Hills and Dales and Fermyn Woods Country Park near the visitor centre. Its beautiful rich colour and strong flight make it well worth looking out for, especially in August and September.

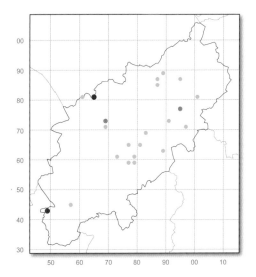

The Clouded Yellow is an irregular immigrant species, in most years being unrecorded or confined to one or two sightings. However, sporadically and quite unpredictably, there are years when there will be a large influx of these butterflies. Usually migrants appear on the south coasts of Britain to disperse through the country later in the year particularly when conditions are favourable for breeding. The first ones appear in June provided numbers have built up on the continent and winds are in the right direction. Home-bred specimens in August will merge with further immigrants from Europe and in late summer it is most likely to appear in Northamptonshire. In exceptional years it will reach the Midlands in the spring and breed here. Such years provide a welcome bonus for local entomologists.

The Clouded Yellow is very distinctive. It should not be confused with the Brimstone since it is a richer, more orange-yellow colour, compared with the sulphur yellow of that species. Also there is a black discal spot on each forewing and deep orange spot in the centre of the hindwings. There is a black band around the margins of each wing of the male which is broken by yellow spots on the female. This is visible in flight which is very rapid, though it often visits flowers, always settling with wings closed.

The underside is deep yellow, showing a black discal spot on the forewing and a metallic silver spot circled in red-brown and shaped in a figure eight on the hindwing. The yellow spots on the marginal bands of the female show through very clearly when the butterfly is viewed against the light. A beautiful variety of the female often occurs in which the ground colour is pale yellow or whitish and is known as the form *helice*. Recent records of this form are from Wakerley and Stanwick (in 1996), Summer Leys (2000), Yardley Chase (2004) and Bradlaugh Fields (2007).

Clouded Yellows frequently feed on flowers

Life Cycle

The Clouded Yellow usually lays eggs on Clover and Lucerne. Changes in farming practice in France, limiting the growth of the latter, were thought to be bringing Clouded Yellow invasions to an end but happily recent years have proved this not to be the case. The eggs are pale when first laid, similar to the Brimstone, then rosy orange and finally purplish just before hatching when about ten days old. The caterpillar when fully grown is green with a white and yellow line along each side, beautifully spotted with pink. The chrysalis is yellowish-green marked with a few black dots held by tail hooks and a silken girdle to the foodplant or nearby vegetation. Neither the adults nor the early stages can withstand the cold or wet of our English climate so that breeding years particularly in the Midlands are few and far between. It has been recorded over-wintering as a feeding caterpillar near Bournemouth.

For most of the nineteenth and twentieth centuries, the Clouded Yellow was a rare immigrant. *The Victoria County History* mentions 1878, 1892 and 1900 as years of abundance in Northamptonshire. In the last of these, it reports 'as many as 17 were taken in one morning in a field near Horton.' *The Northamptonshire Natural History Society Journal* for 1917 comments on its appearance 'after a long interval.' The next major invasion did not occur until 1947, a date which passed into entomological folklore for the profusion of Clouded Yellows throughout the country. The following year it was virtually absent.

Ian Flinders' county survey of 1976-81 mentions three records only, on 22nd August 1976, 25th August 1978 and a maximum of 12 in 1980. However, in 1983 another great 'Clouded Yellow Year', it was known to breed in Northamptonshire after arriving in the spring and was seen in all parts of the county. It was not recorded again until 1992 when it was spotted on a Branch field trip to Wakerley on 17th May, a female being found egg-laying on Bird's-foot-trefoil on an old airfield. This coincided with a massive invasion to the west of Britain at the time. While the butterfly bred on western coasts, it failed to do so in the east which was cold and wet that year and only four were seen in Northamptonshire later in the summer.

Since the 1990s the butterfly has become an almost annual visitor to the county, and has bred more frequently as a result of climate change. On 29th August 1998 a mating pair was discovered at Summer Leys, and in 2006 three separate generations were seen at Hollowell Reservoir and Welford Quarry, indicating breeding throughout the summer from spring immigration. In 2007, despite a good influx into southern England early in the spring, there were only five sightings of single butterflies in our county, attributable to poor weather. The species was on the wing in October here in both 2006 and 2007 and climate change may also be influencing its survival later in the year than previously.

In 2010 and 2011 there have been very few sightings of the Clouded Yellow in the County, demonstrating the unpredictable nature of butterfly migration.

Freshly-laid egg on Bird's-foot-trefoil. It quickly turns to a pink colour

In good years this butterfly is often seen in late summer along the Nene valley

The beautiful helice form of the female

	Jan	Feb	Mar	Apr	May	Jun	Jul	Aug	Sep	Oct	Nov	Dec
Egg												
Caterpillar												
Chrysalis												
Butterfly												

Brimstone *Gonepteryx rhamni*

Male (wingspan 58mm.)

The Brimstone is one of our most interesting British butterflies. It is regarded as the longest-living. Individuals can last for up to eleven months, emerging in July, over-wintering as an adult and often still being on the wing into June the following year. The word 'butterfly' is said to emanate from this 'butter-coloured fly' as it was called, and some sources even attribute the development of anti-freeze to the Brimstone, which may be seen in any month of the year. Only December and January are missing from our recent records in the county.

The Brimstone is the harbinger of spring. A warm spell, usually of more than one day will awaken it from its long slumber. It may well be the first species that most people see early in the year since its primrose-yellow colouring makes the male visible from some distance as it flies restlessly along woodland rides and hedgerows, patrolling a section and doubling back in its search for a female. It flies only when the sun is out, settling under a leaf during cloud cover.

Only occasionally does it pause for nectar, its long proboscis enabling it to gather this from Primrose flowers of which it is said to be the chief pollinator. Sallow blossom ('pussy willow') also provides an early, welcome source of food.

Males spend most of their time in spring searching energetically for females. The latter emerge from hibernation a week or two later than their partners, the exception being in a delayed spring when both sexes appear simultaneously.

Local Distribution and Status

The Brimstone is a common sight throughout Northamptonshire, particularly at the beginning of the spring and again in August when after emerging it frequents flower-rich woodland prior to hibernation. Alder Buckthorn is a common hedgerow shrub and increasingly is being planted in gardens, purposely to encourage this species. Please be aware that Buckthorn berries are poisonous. Numbers do fluctuate from year to year, particularly when there has been a wet spring but there is nothing to threaten the overall future of this common butterfly in our area.

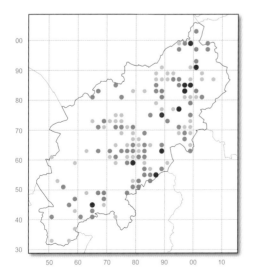

Female

Life Cycle

Mating can be a long drawn-out affair once a female has been found, particularly if a cold spell ensues. A pair flying in copulation on April 14th 1984 were seen to settle down to roost in the early afternoon under a leaf of a Berberis bush in a Northampton garden. They remained in this spot until 24th April, a total of ten days, only turning their wings occasionally towards the sun which shone during this period, even though the weather remained cold. Reference to a pair remaining 'in cop' for a fortnight also appears in the writings of 'BB' so this is by no means unusual. During courtship is the only time the species is seen with its wings open, as the female rests on a flower and thrusts her abdomen into the air.

In summer, the new generation emerges. This time males and females appear together. They immediately set about building up their reserves to see them through the winter. The Brimstone prefers bright sunny conditions and flies when the day is at its warmest. It is rarely seen before ten o'clock and has usually settled down to roost by about three o'clock in the afternoon. During this time it will visit different flowers wild and cultivated. Its long proboscis enables it to extract nectar from teasels, thistles and Buddleia and it is a frequent visitor to gardens where runner bean blossoms are also favoured. Females seem to prefer purple flowers. Both sexes are very photogenic when photographed against the light and when they find a leaf under which to rest as the sun disappears. Winter quarters are the middle of a clump of Ivy, where the Brimstone is remarkably well camouflaged.

The Latin name of the Brimstone means 'angular-winged of the Buckthorn', and the Brimstone is unique among British butterflies in having a concave edge to its hind wings. Prominent veins on the light green underside enable it to blend in with the shiny Ivy leaves, and the pink legs and antennae closely resemble the stalks of the plant.

The light yellow male cannot be confused with any other species. The female is much paler, almost white, but with a pale green hue. At a distance, it could be mistaken for a Large White, though its flight is more purposeful and it has no black markings. The only other sulphur butterfly usually found in our area is the Clouded Yellow which is a richer orange-yellow, much faster flying and has black markings on the edge of the wings.

Eggs are laid singly on the underside of the leaves at the tip of a branch of a sun-facing, but sheltered Alder Buckthorn, in a woodland glade or ride, hedgerow, a bank of a stream adjoining a wood, even a garden if the foodplant is provided. The egg is the characteristic bottle shape of members of the White butterfly family. Several may be seen on one leaf

The caterpillar is a mid-green colour, with a paler underside. When it lies in its familiar position along the mid-rib of a Buckthorn leaf, it is beautifully camouflaged. It eats away at the outside of the leaf from this position

The chrysalis is also a beautiful green colour, hanging by a girdle from the foodplant, where it is superbly camouflaged and difficult to see

A rarely seen mating pair

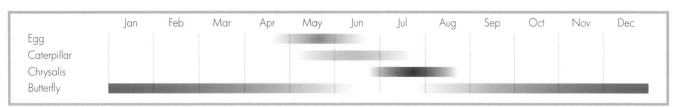

	Jan	Feb	Mar	Apr	May	Jun	Jul	Aug	Sep	Oct	Nov	Dec
Egg												
Caterpillar												
Chrysalis												
Butterfly												

Large White *Pieris brassicae*

Female (wingspan 63mm.)

Local Distribution and Status

The species has always been common and widespread in Northants and its wide-ranging wandering and powers of dispersal, as well as the common distribution of its foodplants especially in gardens, ensure that it is well recorded in most years. Its destruction as a pest by insecticide is counterbalanced by regular immigrations from the continent. Despite concerted efforts to keep it in check where it threatens the farmer, it is not really seriously endangered as a species in our area. In years of large immigration it can be abundant in all habitats as it breeds continuously. This does not always have an impact on numbers the following spring as both eggs and caterpillars can suffer heavy predation from parasitoids.

The Large White, or Cabbage White as it is more popularly known, is perhaps the best recognised of all our butterfly species, largely because of its reputation as a garden pest, its caterpillars being the scourge of many a good crop of cabbages. In favourable conditions it is on the wing throughout the summer, from April until October, in a succession of broods.

The sexes are easy to tell apart, the males having no markings on their white wings other than a large black edge to the forewings which is obvious in flight. Females have two large black spots on each forewing in addition to this. The markings are darker and more extensive in the summer brood. Both sexes of the Large White are extremely mobile and can be encountered in almost any habitat feeding on a variety of flowers and shrubs. In high summer, Buddleias and wild thistles are particular favourites.

Male

Life Cycle

Although the species is referred to as the Cabbage White, egg-laying does not take place solely on garden cabbages; in fact a clump of Creeping Nasturtiums in the flowerbed is much more attractive to Large White females and several egg batches may be found on one plant. Stocks have also been used on several occasions locally but with limited success. In wilder habitat, caterpillars have been found on Hedge Mustard and Kale. Eggs are laid on the underside of leaves in neat batches of up to eighty or a hundred. Females may be observed in the act of laying, perched beneath the chosen leaf and depositing them, one by one, very deliberately.

When the caterpillars emerge, they first eat the eggshells. They seek protection by remaining in a large group only dispersing when fully grown. They exude a smelly green fluid if disturbed and their yellow, black and green markings advertise their mustard content which makes them largely unpalatable to birds. However it is in the caterpillar stage that numbers of the species are most drastically reduced and this prevents the butterfly from reaching even greater pest proportions. Some are accounted for by tachinid flies but most fall prey to the parasitic wasp, *Apanteles glomeratus*, which lays its eggs in the developing body of the caterpillar. As it is about to pupate, it shrivels and dies under a mass of yellow cocoons. Chrysalides which do form are quite easily found under the eaves and windowsills of houses or below the arches of bridges.

The number of Large White butterflies fluctuates considerably from year to year. It is a formidable flier and can migrate vast distances so that in most years the resident population is bolstered by immigrants from the continent. In 1992 some local cabbage fields were alive with Large Whites. Such an increase in numbers was attributed to the use of Oilseed Rape, widely planted in the spring of that year, as a foodplant. Nasturtiums in the garden were laden with eggs to such an extent that there was insufficient food for the resulting caterpillars. Much coverage was given by the local press to this, expressing concerns over the potential damage of such a population explosion.

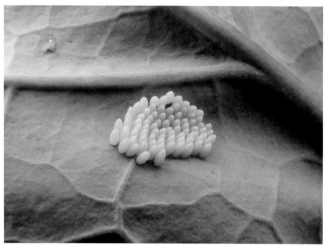
Egg batch on the underside of leaf

Caterpillars feeding on Nasturtium leaf

Female

Feeding on Oxford Ragwort

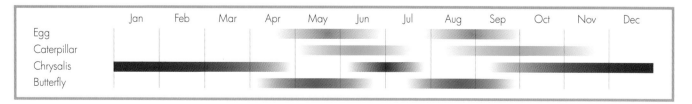

Small White *Pieris rapae*

The Small White is the species of white butterfly most numerous in people's gardens because in some years the Large White is quite scarce, relying on reinforcement from immigration from the continent, and the Green-veined White is more often a butterfly of moister habitats. Very often the three species will be seen together. The Small White is a smaller butterfly than the Large White but this is not always a distinguishing feature as individual butterflies can vary a great deal in size. The male has a black spot in the middle of each forewing not seen on the male Large White and the dark tips on the forewings do not extend down the edges of the wings as they do on the other two species. Butterflies of the second and third generation are more heavily marked than those of the spring brood. The Small White is fond of nectaring but is difficult to photograph as it flits restlessly from flower to flower pausing only for a few seconds. Many different plants are used but it has a preference for paler colours, white and yellow. Lavender is particularly attractive to it.

The Small White does not have quite the same reputation as the Large White for destroying cabbage crops. This may possibly be due to the fact that the caterpillars are solitary and not as easy to spot but it does use the same members of the *Brassica* family as foodplants. In the garden local observers have noticed egg-laying on the leaves of garden flowers such as Nasturtiums, Aubretia and Stocks, though not with the same degree of success.

Numbers of Small Whites are very variable from year to year. A variety of factors can affect its abundance, even from generation to generation, not least of which is a species of parasitic wasp which attacks the chrysalis. It is said that the population is swelled by immigration from the continent but this is not as easy to quantify as in the case of the Large White. Certainly, in 1992, there were very large numbers of the species around, and along with the Large White, it was very common around cabbage fields in the area.

Male (wingspan 48mm.)

Local Distribution and Status

The Small White is a common and widely distributed butterfly in Northamptonshire. It can be found in almost any habitat, ranging from gardens to woodland rides, waste ground, grassland and hedgerows. Widespread use of insecticides stops it from plaguing the farmer's cabbages, but these same crops in fields, allotments and gardens provide a regular supply of foodplants to enable the butterfly to continue to thrive and remain one of our most common species.

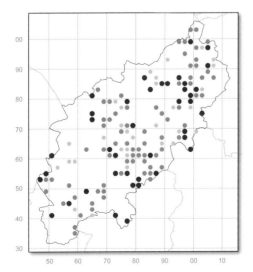

Males have one spot on the forewing

Life Cycle

The Small White spends the winter as a chrysalis and in this stage often can be found under the window sills after caterpillars have been in a garden. Time of emergence may vary considerably according to the temperature and weather conditions in the spring. A mild spell may lead to a chrysalis formed in a very sheltered location hatching in February or even January. In most years the first records come in during March though it reaches its peak numbers around the end of April. Eggs are laid on both the upper and undersides of the foodplant not in batches like the Large White, but singly. They are the characteristic tubular shape of the White family and are pale yellow in colour.

The caterpillar eats the eggshell after first hatching and is yellowish in appearance but soon assumes a green colour which matches the cabbage almost exactly. Camouflage is helped further by the position it adopts along the midrib of a leaf. There is a faint yellow line along the back and a row of yellow spots along the side. On the very similar Green-veined White caterpillar, the spots are replaced by yellow circles around the spiracles. The caterpillars are eaten by a number of birds which find them readily despite their excellent camouflage. Other invertebrates also devour them in their early stages.

The chrysalis can vary in colour from buff with black markings to green with yellow markings depending where it is formed, on a plant, fence or wall. A second generation of Small Whites appears in July and August and in hot summers there may be a third brood in September making it possible to observe the species from March until October, with only short breaks between broods.

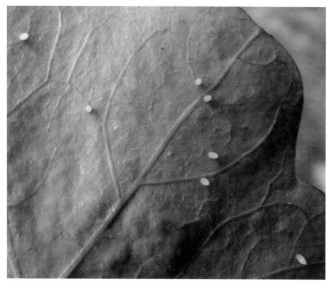

Eggs are laid singly on either side of a leaf

Mating pair

Whites often congregate on manure or mud to take in salts

The female has two black spots on the forewing

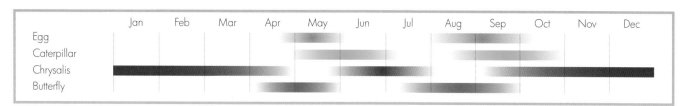

	Jan	Feb	Mar	Apr	May	Jun	Jul	Aug	Sep	Oct	Nov	Dec
Egg												
Caterpillar												
Chrysalis												
Butterfly												

Green-veined White *Pieris napi*

Adult showing the conspicuous 'green veins' (wingspan 50mm.)

Local Distribution and Status

Like the other common Whites, the Green-veined White will appear in almost any habitat. However, it prefers damper situations, particularly in woodland and water margins, such as river banks and the surrounds of reservoirs and reclaimed gravel pits. The species is common and well distributed in Northants but a clear picture of its abundance and distribution is not always available as a number of observers still experience hesitancy in identifying it, especially on the wing.

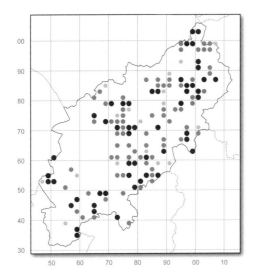

The Green-veined White, though just as common and widely distributed as other white species, is perhaps not as well-known as it should be. Even to the experienced observer, it is notoriously difficult to distinguish from the Small White in flight and at times, individuals can vary greatly in size, miniature specimens being so slow and delicate in flight that they resemble the Wood White if found in the same locality. In damper habitats it is always likely to outnumber the Small and Large White and fly in company with the Orange-tip in the spring. Annual fluctuations in abundance occur, as with all species, and years of low numbers are due often to a long, dry spell, like the one we experienced in 1976.

When seen at rest with wings closed, the Green-veined White becomes easy to recognise. There is an arrangement of black and yellow scales along the veins of the butterfly which make them very prominent. On the upper side the veins are similarly picked out in black more noticeably in the summer brood and the wing tip and the edges of each vein are marked with black. The male usually has one spot on each forewing, very faint in the first brood, while the female has two. The flight of the Green-veined White is a little more erratic than that of the Small White but this is not a reliable identification feature since both species are restless and constantly flitting from flower to flower.

This butterfly emerges in the spring from its over-wintering chrysalis a little later than the Small White though there is considerable overlap in recorded hatching dates. It is most likely to appear first at the beginning of April but often later in the month though a warm spring can bring much earlier emergences. Males are seen first and will be spotted frequently in groups in a damp, muddy area in a woodland ride taking up mineral salts prior to mating. They have also been recorded doing this from a pile of horse manure. Other species of Whites and other butterflies are often found in their company but the Green-veined White usually outnumbers them.

Male

Life Cycle

In gardens this species occasionally lays its eggs on the leaves of Aubretia, but in damper areas such as woodland rides and water edges it will choose Lady's Smock, and in hedgerows Garlic Mustard. It will also select Oilseed Rape where this now grows wild. Unlike the Orange-tip, which shares some of these foodplants, it lays eggs singly on the underside of the leaves rather than below the flower heads. They are very similar in appearance to those of the Small White.

On numerous occasions, particularly in the summer brood, tiny plants only a few centimetres high have been observed as being chosen sites for egg-laying. The caterpillar is not often noticed as it has such cryptic colouring. The lack of a yellow line along the back and yellow circles around the spiracles on the sides distinguish it from that of the Small White. It will rest along the ribs on the underside of the leaf or occasionally may be found on the midrib on the upper surface. The chrysalis too is hard to find as it is usually formed among vegetation and its colours match its surroundings. Again, it is very similar to that of the Small White. Chrysalides of the first generation have a thin outer shell and hatch within a fortnight. Those from the summer brood are thicker-skinned to help them survive the winter.

The flight period of a generation seems to last longer than one of the Small White and the final survivors are more often seen in very tattered condition, their wings frayed to such an extent that they can hardly fly. The butterflies of the first brood fly until mid-June, while those of the second generation normally last from mid-July until September. Sometimes, the species is on the wing until October. It can be found nectaring on a wide range of flowers, particularly thistles and brambles in woodland and yellow *compositae* in more open situations.

This butterfly is often found in woodlands

Female

Green-veined Whites frequently visit garden flowers

Males mud-puddling with Small Whites

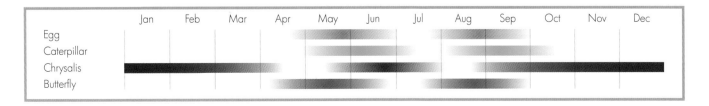

	Jan	Feb	Mar	Apr	May	Jun	Jul	Aug	Sep	Oct	Nov	Dec
Egg												
Caterpillar												
Chrysalis												
Butterfly												

Orange-tip *Anthocharis cardamines*

Male (wingspan 46mm.)

The delicate male Orange-tip cannot be confused with any other species, the orange tips to the forewings being visible from some distance when the species is in flight. On closer inspection these can be seen to have a black edge and a clear, black discal spot. The female can be confused with other Whites unless observed closely; it possesses similar markings to the male but lacks the orange markings. When at rest with wings closed both sexes have a mottled green appearance on the hindwings created by an arrangement of yellow and black scales. Male Orange-tips are very photogenic when on Bluebells or Bugle flowers.

The appearance of the Orange-Tip in spring marks the true arrival of the butterfly season. Its principal habitats are lanes, hedgerows, river banks, damp meadows, roadside verges and woodland rides where its great mobility makes it a common species. May is the usual month to look for it though in recent years the first specimens have begun to appear consistently in April. There is a single generation and by June few are seen, except in late springs when it can be on the wing even into July. Breeding success is determined by the weather since the butterfly only flies in bright sunshine. If conditions are warm, it can still be on the wing into the evening. As soon as the sun disappears behind a cloud it closes its wings. Cow Parsley and Garlic Mustard are common roosts and the cryptic underside colouring creates an excellent camouflage. As the sun returns, it slowly opens its wings before resuming the steady, undulating flight which takes this mobile little butterfly over a wide area. Males will patrol endlessly up and down a set area looking for females. Days of intermittent sun and cloud are ideal for photographing this pretty insect.

Local Distribution and Status

The Orange-tip is a well distributed and common butterfly in our area and its conspicuous markings and tendency to roam over a wide area mean that it is well recorded, though the vagaries of the s pring weather ensure that there are fluctuations in the population of the adults and the number of observations from year to year. It would have been much more numerous in the past but the destruction of hedgerows, drainage of wet meadows, and intensive agricultural practices have changed the scale of abundance.

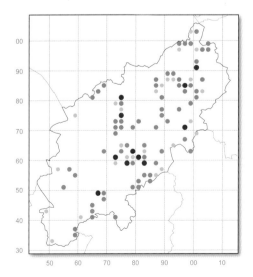

The beautiful underside markings of the male

Life Cycle

A number of foodplants of the crucifer family are used for egg-laying. By far the most successful is Garlic Mustard, but Hedge Mustard provides a good substitute while in damper areas and woodland rides Lady's Smock is also utilised. All three of these are also readily accepted as nectar plants though the species will feed from a wide variety of flowers. Caterpillars have also been found on Tower Mustard, Bastard Cabbage, Honesty, Garlic Mustard and even Oilseed Rape. Eggs have been recorded on Shepherd's Purse, but without success. When first laid, the egg is translucent but turns a bright orange within a few days and is the most conspicuous of any butterfly species as it is laid on the stalk of a plant just below the flower head. Several eggs found on the same plant stalk will be the product of different females. The caterpillars of the Orange-tip are renowned for their cannibalism when young.

The caterpillar usually feeds on the seedpods of its chosen plant. When it first hatches, it is orange with black spines and a black head. Later it becomes greener, until when fully grown it exhibits a fine example of counter-shading, lighter above and dark green below. This prevents it from casting a shadow which would betray its presence as it rests alongside the stalks or seedpods, a position which makes it quite difficult to spot. Even so, many are eaten by birds. The chrysalis is extremely difficult to find in the wild and the butterfly spends around ten months in this stage, including the winter. The mustard oil which it has derived from the foodplants of the caterpillar makes the adult butterfly unpalatable to birds and the bright orange of the male advertises this, an example of warning colouration.

Over-enthusiastic trimming of roadside verges destroys the species in its early stages but cutbacks in Local Authority spending have arrested this trend and the butterfly has actually extended its range in Britain in recent years. A few more wild patches left here and there in parks and gardens would assist it further. Long may we continue to see this harbinger of spring.

A mating pair, male above, female below

The egg is easy to find on Lady's Smock

Female

The caterpillar feeds on the developing seed pods of its foodplant

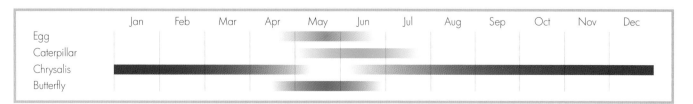

	Jan	Feb	Mar	Apr	May	Jun	Jul	Aug	Sep	Oct	Nov	Dec
Egg												
Caterpillar												
Chrysalis												
Butterfly												

Green Hairstreak *Callophrys rubi*

Adult with the broken white 'hairstreak' line (wingspan 33mm.)

Local Distribution and Status

In the 1980s there were colonies on disused railway lines but these have gradually become too overgrown and the Green Hairstreak has also disappeared from woodland. The north of the county has the best sites in old quarry workings, for example Fermyn Woods Country Park, Twywell Hills and Dales, Collyweston Deeps and Old Sulehay. There have been isolated records in the past from Pitsford Reservoir and it has been seen occasionally in Yardley Chase, but its powers of dispersal are limited.

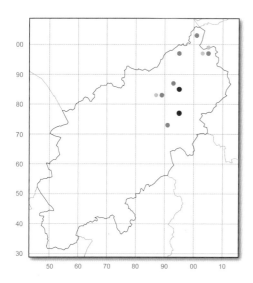

The Green Hairstreak is an intriguing butterfly. When freshly emerged, its hindwings have a rich green velvet appearance which makes it quite unlike any other British species. The green in the mottled pattern on the underside of the Orange-tip is produced by an arrangement of yellow and black scales. In contrast the colour of this butterfly is created by the wing scales absorbing all wave-lengths of light except the green which is reflected. This makes the Green Hairstreak a difficult butterfly to photograph accurately but try under-exposing one or two stops. The species cannot be confused with any other butterfly as its brown upper sides are only seen in flight and it always settles with its wings closed. The sexes are similar. They lack the tails of other Hairstreaks, but possess the broken white line, less often in the form of a continuous white streak, from which the Hairstreaks derive their family name.

Early May (late April in warm seasons) is the time to look for this delightful insect, when the males are to be seen disputing their territories around a suitable Hawthorn or Elder bush. One will take up its favourite perch and will fly up at any intruder. This makes it a relatively easy species to locate. Several may be seen together in flight at the same time jostling for air space like little brown and green leaves in a tumble dryer. Females, in comparison, are less active and are more likely to be seen on the ground crawling over their foodplants in search of a suitable site for egg-laying. The flight period is long, lasting well into June or even July, though individuals soon become tattered from their daily sorties through the Hawthorn scrub.

Normally, colonies are small and most observers will only see a few on any one visit to a site. There is a record in the past of around fifty butterflies being seen on one bush which they were using as a communal roost though such numbers are not usual these days. At the beginning and end of the day the Green Hairstreak will tilt its wings so that they lie almost flat on a leaf exposing the maximum area to the sun to warm the insect. When the sun is low in the sky its light is reflected revealing this insect glowing emerald-like from its leafy perch. Once active it will easily be disturbed on sunny days though its territorial habits make it easy to keep under observation. If the sun retreats behind the clouds it remains on its perch or disappears into the grass unable to fly and again it can be readily photographed.

Life Cycle

Hawthorn blossom is the chief nectar source though it is also attracted to Elder and can be found on the ground, particularly on Bird's-foot-trefoil. This plant is usually the one on which eggs and caterpillars have been found in our area although at Collyweston Deeps, Dyer's Greenweed is also used. Fieldguides attest to a wide range of plants being used. It is more catholic in this respect than any other butterfly in Britain. The caterpillar is a tiny grub, white with brown stripes in the early stages. It is highly cannibalistic after the first moult. It is quite an attractive green with oblique yellow stripes and lateral lines when fully grown. It may then be found feeding just below the flower heads. The winter is spent in the chrysalis stage; all other British Hairstreaks over-winter as eggs.

The butterfly requires warm, sheltered conditions where some scrub has been able to develop but a good ground flora is retained. Disused quarries, abandoned airfields and railway cuttings provide ideal habitats. In *The Victoria County History* the Green Hairstreak was 'rare in 1889-91'. Northamptonshire Natural History Society records describe it as 'common in the Northampton area in 1955' and 'it was frequent, but very locally distributed' in Flinders' 1976-81 survey. In the past woodlands had open, sunny conditions loved by this species but these no longer prevail in modern forestry plantations. A strong colony existed on a disused airfield near Wakerley where it was still seen in 2011, but encroachment of scrub here makes its survival for much longer unlikely. In this same year, after a second successive early spring , the Green Hairstreak was particularly numerous and forty-nine were counted on the Twywell transect on 1st May, the best tally in the county for several decades.

The main threat to the Green Hairstreak is possible landfill and land reclamation of the old quarries. Most of its sites have SSSI status, and are protected by Wildlife Trust ownership or Country Park status and are being sympathetically managed. Butterfly Conservation has started a programme of annual work parties, clearing scrub at Fermyn Woods Country Park and the Whitestones area at Twywell, which should benefit this species, along with the Dingy and Grizzled Skippers with which it is normally found. It is likely to remain very localised it the county but should survive and hopefully thrive at its main sites.

Probing Bird's-foot-trefoil for egg-laying

Fully-grown caterpillar

Chrysalis formed on the ground

Adult on Hawthorn blossom

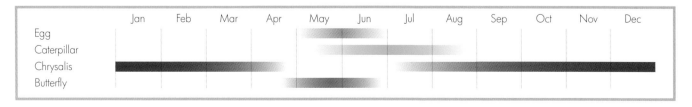

	Jan	Feb	Mar	Apr	May	Jun	Jul	Aug	Sep	Oct	Nov	Dec
Egg												
Caterpillar												
Chrysalis												
Butterfly												

Purple Hairstreak *Favonius quercus*

Female (wingspan 37mm.)

Local Distribution and Status

There is nothing to suggest that the butterfly has ever been less than common in the large forested areas of Northamptonshire, in particular Salcey, Yardley Chase, Rockingham Forest and the Silverstone Woods. Careful searching in recent years has brought new discoveries in smaller woods and copses such as Harlestone Firs and Wicksteed Park.. A few oaks can support a colony, as at Sywell Country Park, Pitsford Reservoir and Farthinghoe Nature Reserve. The distribution map, below, for 2006-10 does not show properly the full extent of the species as there were poor summers in 2006-08 with fewer records than normal and new sites recorded in 2011 are not marked. Diligent searching in any oak woodland in the county during July and August may well provide sightings.

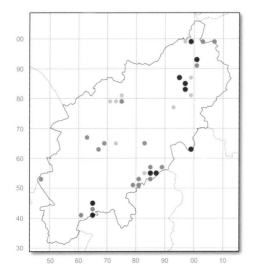

The Purple Hairstreak is not a butterfly normally noted by the casual observer. Those who are familiar with it can claim to have made the transition from beginner to budding lepidopterist for it is a small species, rarely deserting the canopy of the oak woods, flying infrequently and seldom nectaring from flowers. Jeremy Thomas' apt description of Purple Hairstreaks being like silver coins tossed through the air (*The Butterflies of Britain & Ireland*, 1991) would be difficult to better. A few minutes' patient scanning of the tops of the trees on a sunny day will be rewarded in any of our larger oak woods as it is a characteristic member of the butterfly fauna in this habitat. The silvery-grey butterflies flit amid the oak canopy with the typical jerky flight of all the Hairstreaks. As they settle, they can be identified for certain with the aid of binoculars. They are just as likely to be found on other neighbouring tree species on which they feed on the honeydew, Ash being a particular favourite.

This is not to say that the butterfly cannot be observed more closely on occasions. This is most likely when it is newly emerged, or when a female descends to lay her eggs on the lower branches. More often the underside is seen showing the white lines which give the Hairstreak family their name while the corner of the hindwing has an orange eye marking and a tail. This is a defence against predatory birds which mistake them for the insect's real eye and antenna. Swifts have been observed to take the butterflies in flight, discarding the wings.

When the butterfly basks and opens its wings the purple, which gives the species its name, can be seen. The male is almost black on the upper side, only exhibiting a purple sheen when the light catches from the right direction. On the female the purple is restricted to the discal cell and the one below it. This is the only Northants Hairstreak which opens its wings when settled, so this will also identify it from the others when colours cannot be seen against the light.

Sights of this butterfly on flowers are rare though occasionally it has been observed on brambles and thistles. Large numbers have been seen on the woodland floor at times, probing in the mud and settling on low-growing plants near the ground on a windy day in the middle of a ride. This may have been to enable the males to take vital salts prior to mating or could indicate a lack of honeydew in the canopy. Alternatively, the butterflies may have been looking simply to take shelter from the wind though they were numerous among the treetops at the same time. Tattered specimens are also seen on the ground late in the flight period when they have almost lost the ability to fly.

Life Cycle

The Purple Hairstreak usually emerges in early July in our area and only in exceptionally early seasons is it recorded at the end of June. In 2011, it was on the wing on 11th June. Normally the peak is reached towards the end of July but it can still be seen on the wing at the end of August. It can be observed flying well into the evening during warm, sunny weather, a good time to go looking for it. There are even records of it in moth traps.

Of the early stages, the egg is the easiest to find, being laid just below the buds or the end of small twigs on sunny boughs at all levels of the oak. It is conspicuous in winter. Smaller oaks are often favoured. In April the caterpillar hatches to feed on the developing buds and then the leaves where it forms a protective silk web from which to nibble the fresh foliage. Pupation takes place on the ground.

Numbers vary considerably from year to year. Ian Flinders' survey of Northamptonshire (1976-81) indicated that it was very numerous in 1977, with few records for the remaining years. These fluctuations are not so apparent in a series of good summers such as the period in the early 1990s. The species was found in all ten kilometre squares of the county in the Millennium Atlas survey of 1995-99 which was probably attributable to greater familiarity with the species on the part of observers.

The only doubt for the future conservation of the Purple Hairstreak lies in the pressure on forestry for commercial crops but recent environmental initiatives, placing emphasis on restoration of woodland to provide biodiversity and habitat suitable for wildlife, can only benefit it. The move to remove conifers and encourage native trees will hopefully continue to provide plenty of suitable habitat for this interesting species into the future.

The egg is normaly laid beneath an oak bud

The caterpillar is is perfectly camouflaged against the oak buds on which it feeds

The chysalis is found on the ground near oaks and often in association with ants

Male

The silvery-grey underside

	Jan	Feb	Mar	Apr	May	Jun	Jul	Aug	Sep	Oct	Nov	Dec
Egg												
Caterpillar												
Chrysalis												
Butterfly												

White-letter Hairstreak   *Satyrium w-album*

Adult (wingspan 35mm.)

Local Distribution and Status

Surveys for the Millennium Atlas found the butterfly in all parts of Northants. There are a number of well-known spots in Rockingham Forest, particularly in Fermyn and Fineshade Woods. It is also recorded annually in Salcey Forest and parts of Yardley Chase. Colonies can quickly disappear at the hands of Dutch Elm Disease, as happened at Twywell Hills and Dales in 2007 but 2011 brought a number of new site records across the county and any elm would be worth a look during the flight period. Populations can fluctuate widely from year to year.

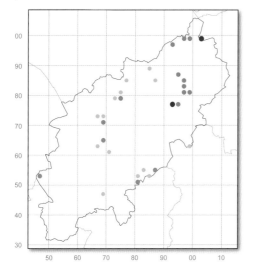

The White-letter Hairstreak has had mixed fortunes during the course of the past century. In *The Victoria County History for Northamptonshire*, it was 'not uncommon in the county, more generally distributed than the Black Hairstreak and occasionally abundant'. Oundle School Natural History Society records show few sightings, apart from '10 at Cotterstock' in 1941. It was described as 'common around Northampton' in 1954. The 1970s saw a major national decline for this species and the Midlands was not exempt from the ravages of Dutch Elm Disease which destroyed the foodplant of the butterfly. Ian Flinders' survey for Northants (1976-81) confirmed its demise; it was recorded in only three 10 km squares during that period and he states 'the study period saw the devastation of the elms due to Dutch Elm Disease'. There were only two records after 1977 in his survey in separate years, 1979 and 1980. He remarks on its absence from known colonies checked after 1977.

However, the butterfly, once thought doomed to extinction because it relied on flowering elms on which to breed, is now known to be able to survive on sucker growth. Its foodplant showed a recovery in during the 1990s and new sites were discovered. At that time the only regular known site was Fineshade Wood but it was recorded in Yardley Chase and woodlands near Brigstock in 1994. In both locations, it has extended its range and can now be found in several areas in these. In Fermyn Wood, on 27th July, 1996, the butterfly defied all traditional textbook accounts. No previous observation of pairing was known but a pair was seen 'in cop' on a privet bush and at least fifty were observed nectaring in the middle part of the day on a patch of thistles extending along the woodland ride for about fifty metres. A shortage of honeydew in the canopy may have brought the butterflies down or several days of cool weather may have been a factor. The species has been seen nectaring from Privet and Bramble flowers as well as thistles, and, at one site, Hemp Agrimony is a particular favourite. On occasions the butterfly has been spotted low on the ground, presumably taking up moisture from the woodland floor.

The elusive nature of the species means that colonies can only be determined on occasions by the detection of the early stages. The egg is relatively easy to find in winter after leaf fall and the caterpillars and chrysalides can also be discovered by looking up into the canopy and seeing them silhouetted against the sky. Indeed, at some sites in Northamptonshire, Hazelborough Forest and Harlestone Firs, records have come only from these early stages.

This butterfly is usually seen in the tree canopy

Life Cycle

The flight period is long, often lasting well into August. The longevity of the species is probably attributable to its sedentary habits. Females, when egg-laying, crawl across the leaves rather than fly and usually deposit eggs singly on the girdle scar which joins the present year's growth with the previous one or just below a leaf bud. This is usually on a sunny, sheltered Wych Elm. Hatching does not take place until the following spring when the flower buds are just beginning to open. The caterpillar is difficult to find while hidden among the developing buds and flowers but can be located when it moves to feed on the leaves as it becomes bigger. At the beginning of June it pupates, often underneath an elm leaf, to produce an adult about a month later.

The White-letter Hairstreak usually emerges early in July although increasingly is now on the wing by late June. This is usually a fortnight later than the Black Hairstreak and a few days before the Purple Hairstreak, though there is some overlap and they do appear in the same sites. Like the Purple Hairstreak, it spends much time high in the canopy on a variety of trees, Ash being a favourite, but is black in flight, compared with the silvery appearance of the Purple Hairstreak and the lighter, more orange tint of the Black Hairstreak. Males appear first, and are generally darker than the females. When seen closely, the species can be distinguished from the Black Hairstreak by a black line inside the orange band on the hindwing compared with a row of dots. The white markings make a W pattern though this is not always clear, particularly on old specimens. The female when newly emerged has very attractive long tails with white tips. Like the Black Hairstreak, the species always rests with its wings closed.

Female egg-laying on Wych Elm

Newly-hatched eggs on an elm bud in early Spring

The chrysalis is often formed on the underside of an elm leaf

Creeping Thistle is a favourite nectar plant

Adults occasionally descend to lower levels

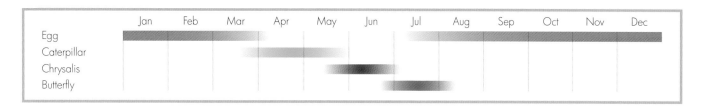

	Jan	Feb	Mar	Apr	May	Jun	Jul	Aug	Sep	Oct	Nov	Dec
Egg												
Caterpillar												
Chrysalis												
Butterfly												

57

Black Hairstreak *Satyrium pruni*

Adult (wingspan 37mm.)

Local Distribution and Status

The Wildlife Trust reserve at Glapthorn Cow Pastures currently holds the most important colony for the Black Hairstreak in the country and this is the best site to observe it though annual numbers can fluctuate greatly. It may also be seen at the adjacent Trust Reserve at Short Wood. At Salcey Forest the species was once widespread with as many as a dozen colonies but in recent years it has almost disappeared there. It is to be found in Fermyn Woods Country Park and part of Fermyn Woods and occurs in smaller numbers in Yardley Chase. A single record was made in Fineshade Wood in 2010 but presence at old sites at Wakerley and Plumpton Wood, which had a colony at the time of Flinders' survey, has not been confirmed. Nine sites were found in a hundred hours of fieldwork by volunteers in 2007. Concerted efforts by recorders in nearby Oxfordshire have unearthed many new colonies, and similar work here, where it is possibly under-recorded, may bring similar rewards.

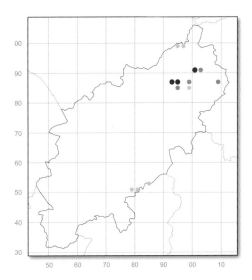

The Black Hairstreak is a localised species in Britain, confined to the East Midland forest belt. It is not easy to determine its exact status for several reasons. Firstly, it is very elusive in its habits, flying only in bright sunshine and making only short sorties among the Blackthorn thickets from which it seldom strays. It is a sedentary species and often hides itself high in the canopy of a neighbouring oak or ash tree. Secondly, its flight period lasts little more than three weeks, from the second week in June until the first days of July. Recorders, with limited time on their hands, tend to concentrate on well-known sites and there may be more colonies to discover. There is a trend towards earlier and earlier emergence; in 2011 it was on the wing on 28th May.

The flight of the Black Hairstreak is very jerky. It occurs in the same localities as the Purple and White-letter Hairstreaks and can be on the wing with both of these, The underside is more golden than the dark appearance of the White-letter Hairstreak or the silver flash of the Purple Hairstreak. Like the White-letter, it never opens its wings at rest, but when seen closely, the Black Hairstreak has a line of black spots along the inner edge of the orange bands on the edge of the hindwing. The 'hairstreak' lines can appear remarkably similar in both species. The female underside is more orange than the rich brown of the male. Like all Hairstreaks, a perfect specimen is only seen in the wild soon after emergence. Attacks by birds and wear and tear from flying among prickly shrubs soon give the butterfly a tattered appearance.

Observations suggest a long daily flight period, individuals being seen as early as 8.30 in the morning and as late as 7.30 in the evening in suitable conditions. In early morning the butterfly can look quite comical as it leans its wings over and appears to be lying on its side in order to expose the maximum surface area to the sun. Privet, Bramble and Dog-rose in particular will attract Black Hairstreaks down to nectar, when they are easy to approach. Females can be seen crawling around the sprigs of Blackthorn to lay their eggs, though seldom, frustratingly, within camera range.

Life Cycle

The egg is by no means as easy to spot as those of the White-letter and Purple Hairstreaks. It is generally laid on 1-4 year old twigs, usually on rough patches on bushes from 2-50 years old. It is pale yellow at first, but becoming greyer as the winter progresses. In its caterpillar stage the butterfly continues to be difficult to detect. In its early days in March, it closely resembles the buds upon which it feeds while its green body with reddish-brown markings is an excellent camouflage against the leaves which it later devours. The chrysalis, which is black and white, closely resembling a bird dropping, is held by a silken girdle to a pad of silk on the foodplant and is regarded as the easiest stage of the life cycle to find.

The Black Hairstreak was discovered in Northants by Rev. William Bree at Barnwell Wold in 1837 and *The Victoria County History* tells us 'it was abundant in woods near Rockingham, Kettering and elsewhere'. An old site was Ashton Wold where it 'flourished in 1949', and it still exists near there. In the same year, the Oundle Natural History Society tells us habitat was destroyed for a colony in Lilford Wood but it was seen at Bearshank Wood and Castor Hanglands where it is still found. Ian Flinders' survey of 1976-81 reported seven known colonies in six 10 km squares. This included a single sighting on Northampton Golf Course and rediscovery at previously known sites but these were said to have balanced disappearances at others.

The onus is on Northamptonshire to continue to conserve the Black Hairstreak for which the county is nationally important. All of its known colonies are at sites where the owners are sympathetic and action is being taken to ensure that they continue to thrive, so its status is not threatened at this time. It is hoped that the above will encourage careful searching by more enthusiasts and will help to monitor existing or old sites and bring to light new ones.

A characteristcic of the Hairstreaks is to angle their wings towards the sun for maximum heat absorption

The chrysalis resembles a bird dropping

Male showing dark scent-brand on forewing

Female feeding on Bramble flowers, one of the main nectar sources

	Jan	Feb	Mar	Apr	May	Jun	Jul	Aug	Sep	Oct	Nov	Dec
Egg												
Caterpillar												
Chrysalis												
Butterfly												

For a few weeks in June every year, visitors from all over the country converge on the Northamptonshire Wildlife Trust Reserve at Glapthorn Cow Pastures to look for the rare and elusive Black Hairstreak. This species has a very restricted range in Britain, and there are other locations in Oxfordshire, Cambridgeshire, Buckinghamshire and Bedfordshire where it may be found, but none can compare with this site for very close views and photographic opportunities.

Crowds gather at the Glapthorn 'hot spot'

A careful management plan has been drawn up to ensure that the Cow Pastures retain suitable habitat for the Black Hairstreaks. A group of volunteers carries out the work on a regular basis through the winter months. Formerly the management consisted of vigorous pruning of the Blackthorn, the caterpillar's foodplant, in early June when the Black Hairstreak was in the chrysalis stage, leaving the brash (the cut branches) in order that the adult butterflies might emerge from it. However, this method proved to inhibit the regeneration of the Blackthorn, so attention is now paid to 'hedge-laying' it. Sheltered glades are created regularly with the encouragement of nectar sources such as wild Privet and Bramble. A particularly early-flowering variety of the latter synchronises perfectly with the flight period of the Black Hairstreak, and two bushes in one of the rides in the centre of the Cow Pastures are a 'hot spot' where the butterflies can always be found relatively easily.

When the Wildlife Trust approached Butterfly Conservation to write a leaflet to be circulated to farmers and landowners in 2007, the successful management at Glapthorn provided the blueprint for advice on meeting the extremely specialised needs of the Black Hairstreak. Where a colony exists, the key is to ensure that there is a continuous cycle of re-growth of the caterpillar foodplant. As it becomes older Blackthorn will die off and

fall over. New habitat must be available to be colonised as areas become unsuitable. The plant regenerates well after cutting and can also spread from existing areas into clearings by sucker growth. Black Hairstreak butterflies do not travel far into new areas, so small colonies can easily be lost by accident or inappropriate management of the Blackthorn.

A true close-up of a Black Hairstreak!

Management and Conservation

Key pointers to conservation of this species are:

- Spray drift in one season could eliminate the colony in a hedgerow and it would not be colonised from elsewhere, so spraying should be avoided.
- Felling of the Blackthorn would eliminate a colony, so removing very small areas of Blackthorn over a number of years is much better than a single large-scale removal. Only in large breeding sites can some felling of Blackthorn be tolerated. If this is necessary, at least 75% should be maintained and subsequent cutting done on a long cycle of 40-50 years.
- If cutting down of nearby areas of wood is required, it is desirable to preserve some tree cover and shelter round the site, particularly round south-facing glades favoured by the butterfly.
- Cutting should be a last resort only in managing Blackthorn in and around a colony. However, if the whole of a small breeding area of Blackthorn is to be cut, this should be done in the butterfly's chrysalis stage, now in mid - late May, as winter cutting will leave nothing for young caterpillars to feed on. Account should be taken of possible breeding birds and knowledge of the species present is also very important (breeding nightingales are present in Glapthorn from early April).
- On woodland edge and hedgerow sites, encourage dense banks of Blackthorn 3-4 metres high. Create sheltered areas by cutting irregular indentations into the Blackthorn.
- Encouraging plants like Bramble and Privet, which produce nectar, will extend the life of the butterfly in sunny spots and so give a longer time for mating and egg-laying.
- Ideally, Blackthorn hedges should be allowed to grow to a large thickness and be treated as scrub blocks.
- If a hedge must be trimmed mechanically, it should be divided into sections and cut in rotation on the largest scale possible.
- Managing ride edges should be done by cutting on a long rotation with numerous indentations which provide sheltered sunspots along the Blackthorn edge and canopy.
- Deer browsing causes damage to Blackthorn. Fencing around regeneration plots has been used on sites where culling does not take place. Alternatively, cut stems can be covered with brash. Laying it like a hedge, rather than cutting it down, creates a barrier against the stock and allows re-growth from suckers, which clear felling does not.
- Before old Blackthorn falls over, it should be 'hedge-laid' and covered with the brash to encourage re-growth from the root. This also protects the new growth from deer browsing and maintains a broad age profile.
- Noting exactly each year where the butterfly is seen is of great value in monitoring and measuring the management process.

During the flight period of the Black Hairstreak a daily count is made at set locations around the wood at Glapthorn. Numbers fluctuate from year to year, depending on the warmth of the spring and as a result of climate change the species is emerging earlier over time, with the first ever May record (28th) in 2011. The elusive habits and short flight period of this butterfly make it difficult to monitor accurately and undiscovered colonies may exist in the county. However, the management at Glapthorn has created a thicket of Blackthorn of varying ages with surrounding Oak and Ash, sheltered glades and clearings, supplemented by ample nectar sources, which make the butterfly easier to see. This constitutes a success story for one of the rarer species.

Old Blackthorn that has twisted , fallen over and died.

Mature Blackthorn laid as a hedge stimulates new growth which in turn makes a good egg-laying habitat for the Black Hairstreak.

The main ride in Glapthorn.

Small Copper *Lycaena phlaeas*

A typical pose of the Small Copper (wingspan 32mm.)

Local Distribution and Status

The butterfly can be found in a variety of habitats – open grassland, waste ground, country lanes, woodland rides, abandoned quarries and disused railway lines. In Northamptonshire, it may be encountered almost anywhere, but most frequently around reclaimed gravel workings, reservoirs and old quarries. Good breeding areas are where the ground is undulating and disturbed by rabbits, allowing the foodplant, Sheep's Sorrel, to flourish, though sometimes Dock may be used. Large leaves in long grass are favoured for egg-laying in spring, smaller ones in more open situations later in the year.

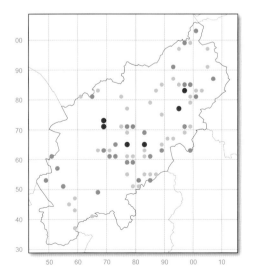

The Small Copper is a distinctive, easily recognised species. It is a lively little butterfly with a quick flight which is difficult to follow but the male is highly territorial and can be relied upon to return to the same spot when disturbed, aggressively fending off any other species which invades its patch. The forewings of both sexes are a beautiful reddish-copper colour on newly-emerged butterflies with black spots and a dark brown fringe, while the hindwings are dark brown with a wavy copper band inside the bottom margin. The wings of the male are more pointed than those of the female which is larger, with rounded wings. The forewing underside is pale orange, spotted with black and the hindwing grey-brown with a red band around the margin.

The markings can show frequent variation in the Small Copper. The spots decorating the forewing are at times unusually small, in other specimens significantly enlarged. Most common is the form *caeruleopunctata* which occurs most often in the later broods of the year. In this aberration there is a row of beautiful blue spots inside the margin of the hindwing. Much rarer is the aberration *schmidtii* in which the normal ground colour is replaced by a creamy white, caused by a recessive gene. This was recorded twice in our area in the 1980s, once at Stoke Doyle near Oundle, once at Ferry Meadows, Peterborough, just outside Northants, and at Bradlaugh Fields on September 2nd 2007.

Small Coppers frequently take nectar from flowers. Thistles and Bramble may be used but it has a particular preference for yellow blooms, notably Fleabane and Ragwort. Towards the end of the season, Yarrow is often chosen.

Life Cycle

The weather conditions each year determine the abundance of the Small Copper. Normally it emerges in late May but can be earlier in a warm spring: it was on the wing on 14th April in 2007. A second, more numerous brood follows in mid-July to mid-August and a third in mid-September, taking the species well into October in most years or even early November. In a hot summer, numbers can build up to high levels. On 17th August, 2006 a record 84 were counted on the dam at Hollowell Reservoir, exceptional for a butterfly usually seen only in ones or twos.

The eggs are relatively easy to spot on small Sorrel or Dock leaves in late summer as small white discs resembling the surface of a golf ball. They are usually laid singly on the upper surface near the midrib where the leaf rises from the stalk. Instances of several on the same leaf occur when the butterfly is particularly numerous over a small area, no doubt deposited by several females. Early in its life the caterpillar betrays its presence by eating small grooves on the underside of the leaf and grey, transparent patches are soon seen where the cuticle has been eaten. As it grows it assumes a slug-like green appearance and becomes more difficult to find, sometimes having pink markings to blend in with its foodplant. The caterpillar will pupate after a month, except in the final generation, when it over-winters. The pale brown chrysalis, with darker markings, is attached by a silken girdle and tail hooks to a leaf or stem low to the ground.

The Small Copper's existence is not seriously threatened in the county and some of its best sites are protected although continued pressure on the countryside for landfill and building will destroy some of its habitat.

Mating pair on Mayweed in Fermyn Woods

The egg is laid on Sorrel and resembles a tiny golf ball

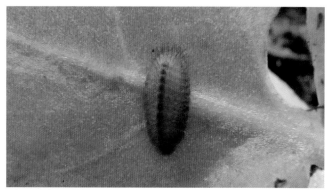

The pink form of the caterpillar, fully grown

Males often have a favourite perch and are always ready to chase away other insects from their patch!

The aberration schmidtii found at Bradlaugh Fields

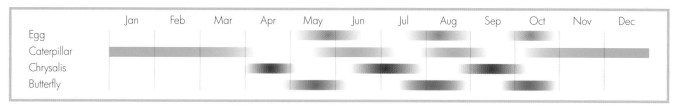

	Jan	Feb	Mar	Apr	May	Jun	Jul	Aug	Sep	Oct	Nov	Dec
Egg												
Caterpillar												
Chrysalis												
Butterfly												

Small Blue *Cupido minimus*

The wingspan of this tiny butterfly is 25mm.

Local Distribution and Status

The typical habitats of the Small Blue are chalk downs, quarries and disused railway tracks where its foodplant, Kidney Vetch, grows amid long grasses and where there are patches of exposed ground for it to regenerate. In Northamptonshire, the foodplant is scarce and records make no mention of this species until a thriving colony was discovered on a disused railway embankment near Brackley in 1986. This site was regularly monitored and the species recorded on an annual basis. It was declared an SSSI, but, almost immediately afterwards public access was denied by the landowner and the site was allowed to revert to scrub. Recently English Nature has undertaken some clearance but its continued presence here is unconfirmed at present. In 1994, caterpillars were discovered on an embankment further down this railway line and the site was found to have good numbers of eggs and adults in June 1996. The Small Blue was recorded here annually until 2008 but sadly may now be extinct.

The Small Blue is our smallest British species. The male is a very dark blue, almost black in appearance, the female slightly browner. This butterfly is difficult to follow in flight, and has a propensity for hiding in long grass. Hence it is not easy to find though its diminutive size makes it distinctive. Both sexes are similarly marked on the underside with black dots on a blue-grey background, much like the Holly Blue. Generally it is very territorial and keeps within a small area, males spending much of their time basking among the vegetation. Females are attracted to yellow flowers of Bird's-foot-trefoil and Kidney Vetch, between bouts of egg-laying on the latter. Emergence can begin from mid-May, though it is most common in mid-June and flies until late June or even July. In southern Britain there is a second brood in August but this is a rare occurrence only taking place in a hot summer. At its only known county site, three second generation adults were found on 3rd August, 2006, the first recorded instance of this in Northamptonshire.

A mating pair

Life Cycle

The egg is the easiest part of the life cycle to find and sometimes the only evidence of the existence of a colony. Even though it is tiny the practised eye can soon locate the pale blue disc which is laid singly in the flower head of Kidney Vetch, often before the buds open. This foodplant is a biennial and in some years is much more abundant than in others. In those seasons when it is scarce, several females lay on the same flower head and, since the caterpillars are cannibalistic, this leads to a shortage of adults the following year. The buff-coloured, slug-like caterpillar feeds on the developing kidney-shaped seeds within the old flower heads in which its head is concealed. Its cryptic colouring makes it difficult to spot, but feeding damage to the seed heads may lead the observer to it. When fully grown it hibernates at ground level before pupating the following spring unless a second brood emerges, though when it does occur numbers are small.

Three separate site visits to its one Northamptonshire location during the poor summer of 2007 recorded only a single Small Blue on each occasion after a good showing the previous year. Such fluctuation can be typical, since Kidney Vetch grows in a two-year cycle being abundant one year and scarce the next. Eggs were also found in 2007 but the embankment is becoming more and more overgrown although the foodplant is still present. Only a single Small Blue was found in 2008 and none since. The site is also under threat from the proposed high speed rail link. Furthermore, here the species is at the northern edge of its main range in southern Britain, some distance from the much larger sites in the Bedfordshire downlands. It is declining nationally and is a priority species in the UK Biodiversity Action Plan. It has a very tenuous position as a county species confined to one known colony so urgent action is required to maintain its status.

Female Small Blue egg-laying

The tiny egg among the flower heads of Kidney Vetch

Bird's-foot-trefoil is a regular nectar source for the Small Blue

A typical pose on a grass stem

	Jan	Feb	Mar	Apr	May	Jun	Jul	Aug	Sep	Oct	Nov	Dec
Egg												
Caterpillar												
Chrysalis												
Butterfly												

Brown Argus *Aricia agestis*

Male Brown Argus (wingspan 29mm.)

Local Distribution and Status

The species has returned to some of its former limestone locations, such as Collyweston Deeps, where Rock-rose is present. There is a strong colony at Twywell Hills and Dales and other good sites, mainly in north and east Northants, are Fermyn Woods Country Park, Summer Leys Nature Reserve and Old Sulehay. Bradlaugh Fields in Northampton is another good place to see it. In these localities, the butterfly should hopefully continue to flourish as they are nature reserves where there is a degree of protection and active management of the habitat. Elsewhere the future of the Brown Argus may be more at risk, with some retraction or stabilisation within this new range. At present its reinstatement as a resident species in the county is most welcome. The Wider Countryside Butterfly Survey has unearthed a number of new sites.

Care needs to be taken in identifying the Brown Argus because the Common Blue shares the same habitats. There is no blue on the upper wings of this species as there is on those of the female Common Blue although the hairs on the body can catch the light and display a blue tinge. When the species basks with wings open the upper sides are a rich chocolate brown and there is a row of bold orange lunules along the margins covering the whole of the wing edge on the female but fading away to the upper edge of the forewing on the male. When the wings are closed, the reliable diagnostic features are the lack of a spot below halfway on the underside forewing and the two black spots near the top outer edge of the lower hindwing forming a colon. In a species not noted for variation, one former Northamptonshire colony regularly contained a large number with reduced spotting on the hindwings.

In flight the male in particular is much smaller than a Common Blue and has a silvery appearance, especially when fresh. The butterfly frequently basks on grass heads and flowers with its wings wide open but at night several can be found perched upside down on grass stalks like the Common Blue. It is easy to examine individuals and make positive identifications when the two species are roosting in this way. The Brown Argus has two broods each year. The first, which is generally small, lasts from mid to late May to mid-June followed by a second, larger brood from late July to late August. In 1997 a small third brood occurred, with one individual recorded in Northampton as late as 4th October, but this is exceptional, as is its early appearance on 25th April 2011.

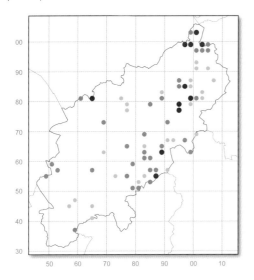

Life Cycle

The main foodplant of the butterfly, Rock-rose, is easily destroyed by ploughing or the use of fertiliser and has disappeared from many sites in the country as a result of intensive agriculture and reduced grazing. This almost certainly led to its extinction in Northamptonshire in the 1950s. The re-colonisation of much of Eastern England in the last decade is partly attributable to the ability of the Brown Argus to use a range of other foodplants, such as species of Crane's-bill, which have flourished on 'set-aside' land and is part of an expansion of range from its traditional downland colonies. Egg-laying is difficult to observe but the butterfly has been recorded using Dove's-foot Crane's-bill in the county. Eggs, pale, blue-green discs, are nearly always laid on the under surface of a leaf on a lush, healthy plant. The caterpillar is a light green colour with pink stripes which provide an ideal camouflage on the shoots of rock-rose. It is usually attended by ants and pupation takes place on the ground beneath the foodplant.

Since 1994, no butterfly can have shown a more dramatic change in status and distribution in our county than the Brown Argus since. Prior to that year the nearest colonies were on the chalk grasslands of the Dunstable area. In Northamptonshire, records had to be traced back half a century to find the most recent confirmed sightings. W.R. Spencer, writing in 1955, describes it as 'common in the Northampton district', a status it shared with the Common and Holly Blues. At Castor Hanglands in a survey of 1961-65 only two or three individuals were seen each year although the foodplant, Rock-rose, was abundant. It was not recorded in Ian Flinders' survey of 1976-81.

With this history, it was a pleasant and welcome surprise when a positive identification of a freshly-emerged male was made at Wakerley on 1st June 1994. This was followed a few days later by a sighting near Weekley Hall Wood. Later in the summer second brood butterflies were to be found at both locations and at several sites in Yardley Chase. At Wakerley and one Yardley site the species could be counted in three figures. Within a few years, the butterfly was found throughout the county. At the same time the butterfly was spreading across the East Midlands and East Anglia, when financial incentives led to the widespread creation of 'set-aside' and populations on traditional downland sites were booming. The Brown Argus is now to be found in most parts of Northamptonshire, usually in areas of newly disturbed ground. The colonies tend to be small in size. It is well worth searching on sites where the more obvious Common Blue is present.

A typical perching pose

Fully grown caterpillar

The underside markings of a resting adult

Courtship display - the female (below) has bolder orange markings than the male

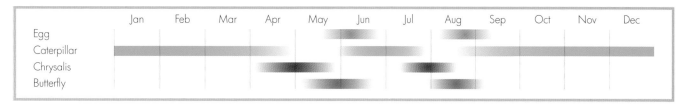

Common Blue *Polyommatus icarus*

Male (wingspan 35mm.)

Local Distribution and Status

The butterfly has always been common in the county but there is little doubt that it has been subject to local extinction during the last half century. Ploughing of land during the Second World War would have destroyed many colonies and our woodlands are no longer open, possessing less sunny, sheltered patches of grassland, leading to a decline in that habitat. Flinders' survey of Northamptonshire for 1976-81 refers to 'colonies decreasing in numbers due to wasteland improvement'. Financial cutbacks which have affected the mowing of roadside verges also mean that it is far less likely to be encountered there nowadays.

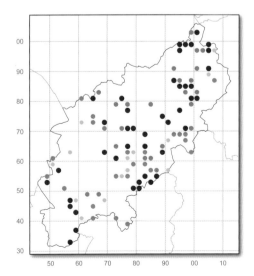

The Common Blue, as its name implies, is the most common of our Blue butterflies in Northamptonshire. The Chalkhill Blue outnumbers it when at its peak in downland locations but this species is not found in the present geographical boundaries of the county. The Brown Argus has superseded it in recent years on some sites, at least temporarily. In gardens the Holly Blue holds sway but the Common Blue may be encountered almost anywhere where its principal foodplants, Bird's-foot-trefoil, Clover and Black Medick have not been shaded out in the natural succession of vegetation. Rough pasture, open woodland rides, old railway lines, abandoned quarries and airfields provide an ideal habitat and it is quick to colonise any new patch of wasteland if there is a colony nearby.

The male is a brilliant lilac-blue when freshly emerged. It has no other markings and the absence of black lines on the white fringes distinguishes it from the Adonis Blue. In any case, the Adonis is not present in our area. The female poses more of a problem of identification. Both blue and brown forms fly within our local colonies and are very variable. The blue females are usually darker towards the wing edges which have a series of light orange lunules. The brown specimens invariably have a dusting of blue scales towards the base which separate them from the very similar Brown Argus. The latter is generally a richer, darker brown with more pronounced orange lunules. Specimens of both species quickly become worn and faded during their short lives in the field and the most reliable way to distinguish them is to inspect the underside. Details on diagnostic features are described in the text on the Brown Argus.

The Common Blue is usually on the wing from the second half of May though in an advanced spring it can emerge near the beginning of the month. Sightings on 26th April 2007 were exceptional. Numbers build up to a maximum in early June and there is usually a lull in late June and early July before the more numerous second brood appears. This has a long emergence and the species is often seen into September or even early October. The males are very territorial, choosing a perch a little higher than the surrounding vegetation from which they will chase off other males and even other much larger species of butterflies. Females are generally less conspicuous unless egg-laying or feeding. Both sexes frequently nectar from flowers. Marjoram, Bird's-foot-trefoil and Fleabane are favourite ones. At night and in dull weather the species rests communally, the butterflies perching, heads down, several on the same grass stem. Early morning or late afternoon when they are like this is a good time to visit a habitat and test out the identification features mentioned above. As the sun comes up they will open their wings in unison and provide the ideal opportunity to photograph a group together.

A female showing the underside markings

Life Cycle

The eggs of the Common Blue are relatively easy to find. They are light grey discs with a raised network and stand out on the tender young leaves of the foodplants as they are usually laid singly on the upper surfaces. The empty eggshells can also be seen for a time since they are not eaten. The caterpillar is quite secretive and is easily disturbed from the foodplant when young. It has a greenish-yellow body at this time and has yellowish lines as it matures. When fully grown it has a black head and bright green body with darker green lines along the sides. Caterpillars from the first brood will pupate after about six weeks while those of late summer will hibernate after the second moult until March. The chrysalis, which keeps part of the larval skin, is formed on the ground beneath the foodplant. One fully-grown caterpillar was found at Finedon attached to the underneath of a small piece of limestone where it was about to pupate.

The Common Blue fluctuates enormously in numbers from one year to the next. A warm, wet spring will provide a large second brood later in the summer, which will in turn lead to success the next year. In 2006, after a very warm spell in July, a small third brood hatched. In 2007, after its earliest ever emergence, extremely poor midsummer weather meant the second brood was virtually non-existent. Drought years can also have a profound effect since the foodplants can become withered and die in the heat. On some sites populations have been diminished by huge increases in rabbits which have depleted the ground vegetation. The Common Blue is not a threatened species but current practices of Man in our countryside make it increasingly likely that, in the future, it may be largely confined to sites which are managed and protected, a marked contrast to the abundance which it enjoyed sixty years ago. In the future, warmer temperatures and more extreme weather events may well have an impact, pushing its range further northwards.

Female egg-laying on Bird's-foot -trefoil

The egg is laid on the upper side of a leaf

Mating pair, female on the left, male on the right

A newly-emerged male taking nectar

The blue form of the female

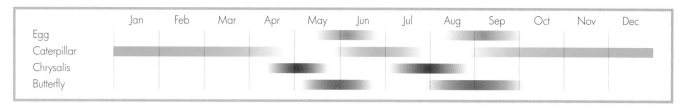

	Jan	Feb	Mar	Apr	May	Jun	Jul	Aug	Sep	Oct	Nov	Dec
Egg												
Caterpillar												
Chrysalis												
Butterfly												

Chalkhill Blue *Polyommatus coridon*

Male (wingspan 38mm.)

Local Distribution and Status

A single specimen recorded in Salcey Forest on August 8th 1976, after strong south-westerly winds, is the only record in Ian Flinders' survey of 1976-81. Individuals can be found some distance from existing colonies, as with sightings of males in Salcey (7th August 1982 and between 10th and 15th August 1997) and Yardley Chase (14th August 2003). Another was seen in Ring Haw on 14th August 2010. A colony did exist for some time just inside the county boundary at Bedford Purlieus but little suitable habitat exists in Northamptonshire for it to become established permanently. The nearest colonies to Northamptonshire are in the Dunstable area of Bedfordshire and Devil's Dyke and the National Nature Reserve at Barnack Hills and Holes in Cambridgeshire, where it is thriving.

The male Chalkhill Blue should not be confused with any other species in our area. It is the largest of the blues seen locally and is a pale, milky-blue colour compared with the much darker, brighter blue of the Common Blue. The Holly Blue is far less likely to occur in the same habitat. There is a dark edge to the wings and the white fringe is chequered. The female is brown with bands of orange lunules towards the wing edges, more pronounced on the hindwings and again with a chequered white fringe to the wings which will separate the Chalkhill Blue from any other butterfly when they are closed. There can be much variation in this species, a fact which led to considerable collecting in the past.

Wherever Horseshoe Vetch grows on south-facing slopes, sheltered valleys or abandoned chalk pits the Chalkhill Blue may be found. Although not often seen in the many thousands which festooned the hillsides in pre-war days, a magnet for keen observers and collectors, it still exists in good colonies in southern England. A strong population has built up at Barnack Hills and Holes only a few miles from our county. In 2006, nine Chalkhill Blues were recorded at the nearby Wildlife Trust Reserve at Southorpe Paddock. It is included here as the last of these sites was in the vice county of Northants for recording purposes.

There is one generation a year which usually begins in mid-July, peaking in mid-August and often lasting a couple of weeks into September. Males, when they first emerge, particularly on good sites, will gather in groups to 'mud-puddle' on a patch of wet ground or on a pile of animal droppings. The species generally flies low over the ground and nectars especially on purple flowers of Scabious, Knapweed, thistles or Marjoram. At night, in common with other species of Blues, adults will roost communally among the grass stems. Females are less active, but can often be found feeding among the males.

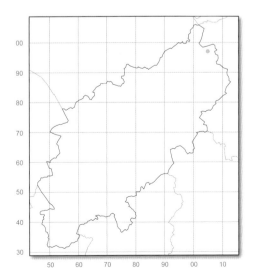

Life Cycle

The Chalkhill Blue lays its eggs on Horseshoe Vetch, the only foodplant of this species, where it is found growing well among surrounding grasses. The female crawls on the ground to find suitable leaves and lays her eggs singly on the stalks and stems and sometimes on surrounding vegetation. The egg has a particularly hard shell, necessary for it to survive the winter, during which it often falls from the plant to the ground. It does not hatch until April. The caterpillar is light green in colour with two yellow broken lines along the back and a yellow line along each side. It is nocturnal, appearing to feed on the leaves at dusk and makes itself very attractive to ants by secreting chemicals. Indeed, the chrysalis may well be found concealed within ant nests and has the capacity to make a sound which will draw the ants towards it.

The Chalkhill Blue declined markedly in the 1950s when the outbreak of myxomatosis led to the loss of rabbits, allowing the downland scrub to develop to the detriment of the species' breeding. Some sites on flatter land disappeared when they were ploughed and fertilised. It was at about this time that the butterfly would have become extinct in Northamptonshire, for which early records are somewhat sketchy. It was always at the extreme of its British range in the county in any case. It is described as 'very local in the neighbourhood of Barnack' in 1937, while there were 'considerable numbers in its restricted localities about 8 miles from Oundle'. Records appear in the journals of the Northamptonshire Natural History Society of 1952 for Bedford Purlieus on August 8th 1917 and July 28th 1945.

Female

Males often congregate to feed on animal faeces

At rest, showing the underside markings

A male feeding on Marjoram

	Jan	Feb	Mar	Apr	May	Jun	Jul	Aug	Sep	Oct	Nov	Dec
Egg												
Caterpillar												
Chrysalis												
Butterfly												

Holly Blue *Celastrina argiolus*

Female (wingspan 35mm.)

Local Distribution and Status

This mobile butterfly can be seen throughout the county in a good season when most gardens and churchyards provide records. However, in other years it is difficult to locate though it is always recorded annually. Clearance of Ivy in the autumn occasionally may destroy the early stages, but the Holly Blue's ability to move from one area to another and thrive in a wide range of habitats with, at times, a diversity of foodplants, should ensure its continued survival. Local observers have noted much of interest about this species but a great deal still remains to be discovered about this attractive and fascinating butterfly.

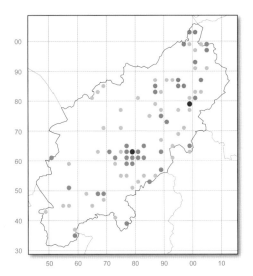

The Holly Blue is renowned more than any other butterfly for its annual fluctuations of numbers. Approximately every five years there is a dramatic explosion of the population and even casual observers remark upon, "little blue butterflies flying around the garden." In the year following such a peak the species occurs in reasonable numbers before becoming scarce or almost absent for a year or two. The cycle is dictated by an ichneumon wasp, *Listrodomus nycthemerus* which lays its eggs in a young caterpillar. These then develop in the caterpillar and the chrysalis and a generation of wasps replaces most of the butterflies.

In terms of identification, the Holly Blue can be distinguished from other Blues early in the year as it appears well before the Common Blue and frequents gardens, parks and woodland rather than open ground. When seen at rest the Holly Blue has silver-blue undersides with black spots. It is similar to a Small Blue but larger. In any case, the latter is found in one location only in Northamptonshire. There are no orange markings. The butterfly is well camouflaged among the shiny leaves of the Holly and Ivy. The upper sides are blue, fringed with black on the forewing tips on the male with a distinct chequering to the fringes. In the female, the forewings have a broad band of black towards the edge which is more extensive in the summer generation. The species only flies in bright sunshine and only basks with wings open, usually at 45 degrees, on cool days or when warming up after a cloudy spell.

The Holly Blue shares with the Hairstreaks a fondness for feeding on honeydew from leaves of various shrubs and trees. It will, however, use a variety of nectar sources, including the blossoms of Holly and Ivy, no doubt assisting in the pollination of its foodplant. Bramble is a particular favourite and churchyards with wild corners and both Holly and Ivy are ideal places to look for this fascinating butterfly. Less appealing is the penchant of the males for taking mineral salts from faeces prior to mating. One has been observed to feed undisturbed from a bird dropping on newly-cultivated garden soil for over half an hour and they will imbibe from the smelliest pile of dog dirt. Muddy edges of ponds and tracks provide a similar food source.

At rest, showing the underside markings

Life Cycle

Holly is the usual foodplant in spring and eggs, which are tiny, light blue discs, are laid just below the flower heads. The caterpillars are difficult to see when quite small on the developing berries. They curl around a berry and leave a characteristic hole in the centre. Careful inspection near to this feeding damage will usually lead to their discovery but they blend perfectly with their surroundings. Like many Blue species, they are attended by ants. Chrysalides have been found in the wild under a stone in the ground and in a curled-up leaf at the back of a clump of Ivy on a wall.

This is the only British butterfly to change its foodplant with the season. In late summer eggs are laid underneath the flower heads of the Ivy. Several have been recorded on one flower head, but these are the product of different females in years of abundance. The first caterpillar to hatch will eat the rest, a way of ensuring there is sufficient food to guarantee survival. In the wider countryside some interesting foodplants have been recorded by observers. Dogwood is regularly used where Holly is absent and Wild Liquorice (Milk-Vetch) has been utilised in North Northants. In gardens Pyracantha provides a suitable alternative for Ivy. Egg-laying has been seen on Alder Buckthorn and Portugal Laurel has proved successful on one occasion.

Early sources describe the Holly Blue as uncommon, this no doubt being based upon years when it was the low point in its cycle. Later surveys which encompass several seasons refer to the years of abundance. Flinders' survey for Northamptonshire for 1976-81 describes it as uncommon but notes 'an explosion of numbers in the s pring of 1979, with few butterflies before or since'. 1990 was an outstanding year for the species. Warm weather early in the year brought emergence forward on 1st April. This was followed by ideal conditions for egg-laying and there was a continuous supply of butterflies until September with only a short period between flight periods and vast numbers in the summer brood. In early August around 50 were seen along a 100 metre stretch of hedgerow in Eastern Northampton. Normally the species is only seen in ones and twos. In 2007, one of the worst summers on record, the Holly Blue was found throughout the county in both the first and second broods, bucking the trend of most species and an unprecedented small third brood saw it on the wing on 2nd November. Nationally it is a success story, recently spreading as far as Scotland, where it is now breeding.

Mating pair, probably newly emerged from the Ivy on which they are perched

Eggs on Alder Buckthorn, most likely laid by separate females

Caterpillar of the second brood on Ivy buds

Male

Female

	Jan	Feb	Mar	Apr	May	Jun	Jul	Aug	Sep	Oct	Nov	Dec
Egg												
Caterpillar												
Chrysalis												
Butterfly												

White Admiral *Limenitis camilla*

Adult (wingspan 64mm.)

Local Distribution and Status

The White Admiral is once again a regular in the woodland of Northamptonshire in July and early August, its reappearance in the last two decades or so coming after periods of absence mixed with times of abundance. The future of this species seems relatively secure at the moment as developing plantations provide the half-shaded but sunny conditions for the butterfly. As these woods age and mature, they become too dark. The maintenance and harvesting of conifers in cycles and the move towards restoration of more broad-leaved woodland should ensure that the habitat remains for this graceful insect in most of our larger woods.

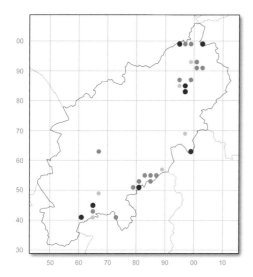

The graceful, gliding flight of the White Admiral in most of our larger woods is a sight to look out for in the middle of summer. The males and females of this species are both dark brown with a clear white band across all four wings, the latter being slightly larger and lighter. The underside is perhaps the most attractive of all British species, being beautifully patterned in orange-red, white, black and blue-grey. Only the Purple Emperor, which flies in similar habitats, can be mistaken for this species but it is altogether larger with a more powerful flight and more pointed wings.

Aberrations of the White Admiral are recorded in most years when the numbers are high, and are well worth looking for. Occasionally specimens of the totally black aberration *nigrina* are seen, along with the more common *obliterae* which has reduced white banding. This can vary from a slight reduction to almost total absence. 2006 was a particularly good season for these. Extremes of cold in the first few hours of pupation give rise to these aberrations, both of which have very attractive undersides.

In most years, the single-brooded White Admiral appears in late June to early July, though in a warm spell it can emerge as early as mid-June. Numbers usually reach a peak in mid-July. A few last until mid-August but their wings soon become tattered as a result of flights among Bramble, a favourite nectar source. Late May and early June weather plays a key part in dictating numbers in a given season. A warm spell at this time means that the caterpillars develop quickly and the chrysalis stage is short-lived, thus reducing time for birds to eat these stages. Numbers are then high, as in 2006. A cold, wet June leads to high predation and few adults are then on the wing, perfectly illustrated by the 2007 season.

Several butterflies can often be found on a sunny, sheltered Bramble patch. Other sources of food are thistles and umbellifers while the White Admiral will take honeydew from a variety of trees. In the early part of its flight period and in the morning in particular, like the Purple Emperor, the species comes down to the ground to take sustenance from mud or animal droppings on stony paths though not quite as prominently as its larger cousin.

Bramble blossom is a favourite nectar source

Life Cycle

Mating behaviour is not likely to be seen, reputedly taking place in the forest canopy. Eggs are laid on straggly pieces of Honeysuckle and look like minute sea-urchins. They hatch after a couple of weeks and the young caterpillar feeds, often into October. Its eating is characteristic. It nibbles the leaf at right angles from the tip while leaving the midrib untouched and projecting. As autumn arrives, while it is still quite small, it constructs a shelter called a hibernaculum for the winter, using a leaf of the foodplant. Feeding resumes with the onset of spring. The caterpillar is brown at first but turns green in its final stages, camouflaging itself by resting with its head and tail in a curve on a tender leaf. The chrysalis is very beautiful, hanging like a shrivelled leaf, twisted and browning, with metallic spots which imitate rain drops.

Caterpillar on Honeysuckle leaf just prior to pupation

Historically the White Admiral has enjoyed fluctuating fortunes in our county. In 1882-3, the species was recorded in Northamptonshire in Sywell Wood and Lilford Wood but it was scarce at the turn of the twentieth century. It is not noted in the records of Castor Hanglands for 1961-65, though it was 'usually seen in the larger woods flying along the ridings' in the Northampton area in 1954. Flinders' survey for Northants (1976-81) shows only four records with a maximum of three butterflies in 1979. The reasons for its scarcity he states as a 'dramatic decline in numbers to virtual extinction in the 1960s, most likely due to forestry management and spraying'. He felt that, given favourable conditions, it would return as there were colonies near to the county boundary.

This butterfly can be found basking on a leaf to warm up in the sunshine

Shortly after, a series of good summers and mild winters heralded its dramatic return. There were a few records in the early eighties, and it returned to Salcey, its former stronghold, in the warm summer of 1983. Its dispersal to other areas, the Silverstone Woods and the Rockingham Forest area, soon followed. The abandonment of coppicing, which had so deprived the Fritillary butterflies of their habitat, promoted suitable conditions for the foodplant, Honeysuckle, to thrive. It is still found in good numbers in these woods today.

An adult imbibing minerals and showing the beautiful underside of this species

Adults often bask with wings open

This aberration obliterae was seen in Fermyn Woods in 2006

	Jan	Feb	Mar	Apr	May	Jun	Jul	Aug	Sep	Oct	Nov	Dec
Egg												
Caterpillar												
Chrysalis												
Butterfly												

Purple Emperor *Apatura iris*

The Purple Emperor is the jewel in the crown of Northamptonshire butterflies. The colony in Fermyn Wood is now regarded as the largest and most important in the country and visitors from the length and breadth of England make an annual pilgrimage there to see it. The purple sheen shown when a male flashes its wings gave it various names among naturalists in the past, such as 'His Imperial Majesty' and 'Sultan of Morocco'. This only shows on both sides when the light catches it at just the right angle. Normally, it only gleams on one side. The Emperor can be confused with the White Admiral but has smaller white markings and the white band is thinner. Its larger profile, more angular wings, its powerful soaring, rather than gliding flight and flashes of purple should distinguish it. The female lacks the purple but is a very large butterfly. When the wings are closed, the large eye spot on the reddish-brown and pinkish-grey forewing is a distinguishing feature. Aberrant specimens, with reduction of the white bands, usually rare, have been recorded in Fermyn Wood in each of the last three years (2009-11)

This species emerges from late June, a few days after the White Admiral, and flies throughout July. The best time to see it is in the second week of the month when the males descend to the ground, their wings flashing open and closed as their long, yellow proboscises extract mineral salts from stones, puddles or animal droppings. The nutrients obtained are essential for them to mate successfully. Bright, shiny objects also attract the butterfly, which will settle on car windscreens. In the past, the Purple Emperor was much sought after by collectors, who lured it from the treetops with the putrid carcasses of dead animals. This is not really necessary as newly emerged males come down readily to procure vital minerals prior to mating.

Male (wingspan 75mm.)

Local Distribution and Status

The Purple Emperor's re-establishment in Northamptonshire at present represents a success story. It requires a large, continuous tract of mature woodland through which it can fly over an extensive breeding ground such as exists in the Fermyn Woods complex, the Silverstone Woods, Salcey Forest and Yardley Chase. It is now recorded in all of these. Removal of ride-side sallows can destroy its breeding habitat, but it will survive as long as these are allowed to regenerate. Butterfly Conservation will seek to work closely with the Forestry Commission in the future to ensure that this magnificent butterfly continues to thrive.

Most observers only see the butterfly on the ground but its daily aerial activity is worth watching. After feeding on the ground, males use several strategies for enticing females. They may perch on 'master trees' awaiting a female to come into their territory, while at the same time driving off rival males. Two major assembly points have been discovered in Fermyn, one centred on Black Poplar trees and another around oaks. Alternatively, they may indulge in 'sallow searching' for females newly emerging or 'oak edging', intercepting them as they fly around the canopy of these trees. Once an unmated Empress comes into range, she is followed and enticed to the topmost branches where she is swiftly mated. In 2007 two pairings were observed high in the canopy, one timed to last for 3 hours 40 minutes. Matthew Oates has spent a lifetime studying *iris* in depth, using Fermyn as a base for a number of years. Visit www.thepurpleempire.com for current observations throughout the country during the flight period and to follow this butterfly's early stages through the remainder of the year.

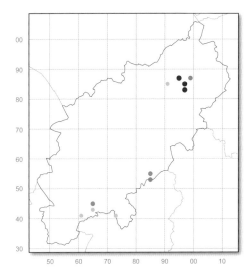

Purple shows on both wings only when viewed at the right angle

Life Cycle

The egg of the Purple Emperor is quite attractive, like an upturned pudding basin with fourteen longitudinal keels. It is green when first laid but a purple ring soon develops round the base. This extends to the tip of the egg when it is due to hatch. Broad-leaved Sallows on the edge of rides, sheltered by large trees behind and partly shaded from the hot sun, are usually chosen. The eggs are laid singly on the upper surface of the leaves, well inside a large sallow, and usually high up.

The tiny caterpillar crawls to the tip of a sallow leaf and takes a position facing inwards towards the stalk. It later develops horns and is well camouflaged throughout the ten months of its life. In winter it turns a muddy brown colour and is attached by a mat of silk to the fork of a branch or a leaf scar. It resumes feeding in March. The chrysalis is formed in early June and, with its pale green colouring and white markings, closely resembles a leaf of the foodplant to which it is attached.

The Victoria County History for Northamptonshire mentions that the Purple Emperor occurred commonly in the great oak woods in the neighbourhood of Rockingham, Kettering, Weekley Hall Wood and Geddington Chase, in Whittlebury Forest, Salcey Forest, Yardley Chase, Sywell Wood and elsewhere in the south and north of the county. A collector caught 80 specimens from a Midland wood between July 11th & 24th 1857. The Northamptonshire Natural History Society, long before the conservation movement was established, condemned this, stating that 'it will no longer survive the wasteful attacks made on him, notably for purposes of gain and barter.' A further reference in an article *The Butterflies of Bucks 1790-1969* tells us that it was still around in Salcey in the 1960s but disappeared from there and the rest of the county at that time. Ian Flinders' survey of 1976-81 revealed no evidence of its presence in the county despite extensive searching in suitable habitats. He mentions unsuccessful attempts to reintroduce the species, no doubt referring to the lifelong ambition of 'BB', who had a particular affinity with the Emperor and its fascinating life cycle and constantly wrote of his desire to see it re-established in his native county.

The butterfly began to be seen again in the early 1980s in one of its old haunts in Fermyn Woods near Brigstock. Whether it owed its reappearance to the release of captive stock ('BB' lived nearby) or whether it had survived as a small relict population, below observation level, is uncertain. By the end of the 1980s the species was certainly breeding here without assistance. It has now extended its range within the large network of woods which stretches from Thrapston to Corby where the extensive growth of Sallow provides ideal habitat. It can also be found in smaller numbers in the Silverstone woods and has been re-discovered in Yardley Chase (2009) and Salcey Forest (2011).

Aberration lugenda seen in Fermyn on 4th July 2010

The 'eye' on the wing can act as a deterrent against predators

The female has larger white bands than the male (wingspan 84mm.)

Eggs are laid on the top of sallow leaves which are within shade

	Jan	Feb	Mar	Apr	May	Jun	Jul	Aug	Sep	Oct	Nov	Dec
Egg												
Caterpillar												
Chrysalis												
Butterfly												

Denys Watkins-Pitchford, who wrote under the pseudonym 'BB', was an eminent naturalist-writer who was born in Northamptonshire and spent his life here. His fascination for the Purple Emperor (*Apatura iris*) began when he was young -"I used to spend hours reading about it in my Frohawk's *British Butterflies*, looking longingly at the colour plate which showed the insect in all its regal purple sheen, and I used to think that the outside of its wings was even more beautiful, with its greenish whorls and marblings and the rich coloured eye on the forewing tips." 'BB' began a persistent search for it, when he found that it was 'most frequent in Northamptonshire and Lincolnshire.'

Old sites for the butterfly were Barnwell Wold and the woods around Polebrook, while in Geddington Chase in 1878, a man had captured over a dozen in a single day. 'BB' also mentions newspaper cuttings referring to an Emperor being seen and captured at Yardley Chase. A well-known Victorian entomologist, the Rev. William Bree, rector of Polebrook, once caught a specimen in his hat down a riding in Ashton Wold. On a visit to his church, 'BB' surmised that he must have preached on many a hot summer afternoon, his mind no doubt wandering to the rides of the adjacent woods where the Purple Emperor was found. He tells us the butterfly was still at Ashton in 1943, but only as a rarity.

'BB's early searches for the Purple Emperor found much of the habitat unsuitable. In 1940 while wandering round Monk's Wood, a former good site for it, he describes meeting an entomologist of the old school with his Emperor net 15ft high, and he was amused by his pretended ignorance, while 'his sly thirst for information suggested he was a professional collector.' After a brief view of his long sought after prize in Salcey Forest, 'BB' finally 'came face to antennae with *iris*' properly for the first time in 1946. He accompanied Stuart Humfries, an eminent eye-surgeon, to a wood in Oxfordshire. Having seen a Purple Emperor settle high up on an oak leaf, he and Humfries seeing a timber truck with wheels nearby dragged it under the tree, so that 'BB' could reach with his net. He made a sweep for it but it had vanished into thin air. The same day a worn male circled twice round his head and settled on his knee.

It is clear from his writing that oak woodland was 'BB's favourite habitat, and he extols the wide rides bathed in hot sunlight on a July afternoon, the cool shadows banding the rides, the sound of the turtle doves and bullfinches, humming flies and the smell of the Meadowsweet. Subsequent visits to Salcey Forest brought many happy sightings of the Purple Emperor before spraying to eliminate Oak Tortrix moths led to its extinction in the 1960s. In 1948, he saw a female laying an egg and plunged into a ditch to pull down a sprig of Sallow to inspect it. Salcey also inspired his book *Brendon Chase* and here in a shady ride one day, he encountered John Phillips, a Kettering surgeon who taught him how to find the butterfly's eggs successfully.

Eggs can be found on the lower branches of large Sallows but climbing high into the upper branches may yield even more. One eminent entomologist, a very big and heavy man, fell and injured himself so badly that he died later. 'BB' regarded the death of a well-known collector, killed after falling in a ditch while searching for eggs, as a fitting end, and was prepared to take the risk on many occasions. Once able to gather eggs, he admitted that the '*iris* bug' had bitten even deeper and he vowed to tend the caterpillars through the winter. It became his mission to reintroduce the Purple Emperor to its ancient stronghold.

In his book *Ramblings of a Sportsman-Naturalist*, 'BB' describes the life cycle of this beautiful insect in great detail and reveals what a marvellous observer and entomologist he was. On hatching the caterpillar eats the eggshell and then moves to the leaf tip where few predators explore and where the moisture drains off to protect it. He describes the minute beetle *Anthocoris nemorum* and its devouring of the tiny caterpillars. Much skill is needed to protect them from other enemies, such as spiders and earwigs, and to tend them so that they survive the winter.

In 1973, 'BB' tells us that he released 25 adult Purple Emperors into 'the Chase'. It is not clear exactly where he means, but this was most probably the ride in Fermyn Wood known as 'Emperor Ride', a few minutes' walk from his home. The following year, he found eggs to confirm that they had indeed bred there. On July 28th 1978 he found 18 eggs and a female intent on laying. In 1980, he refers to them as, "the Purple Emperors of mine (they really *were* mine, of my own stocking, for as far as I know, *iris* did not occur in this forest in recent years)."

BB watches the release of his butterflies into "Emperor Ride" in the mid 1980's photographed by Jack Steward

As a result of climate change the Purple Emperor is extending its range nationally. It has become widespread in Oxfordshire, another old haunt, and has been recorded in Warwickshire, Suffolk and Cambridgeshire in recent years. Sallow regenerates quickly on the clay soils of our county and Fermyn Wood has the perfect conditions for it, the habitat developing particularly after 'BB's death in 1990. What role the writer played in its current expansion is difficult to establish. It may be that the butterfly was there all along and his intervention helped the population to reach the level where it began to be seen more readily. It is nonetheless a source of great pleasure to feel that current butterfly enthusiasts are treading in the same woodland rides into which he ventured and to reflect that his cherished dream of seeing 'His Imperial Majesty' flying there again is now an ongoing success, a fitting monument to this great naturalist.

In the 1982 season, he only found two eggs as the vision in his right eye had become impaired to the extent that locating them was becoming too difficult. By then, however, his labours had begun to bear fruit. Ian Flinders' survey of the butterflies of Northamptonshire 1976-81 had deemed the Purple Emperor extinct but subsequent to this, local enthusiasts had begun to find it again in the woods around Brigstock. It could be seen only a few hundred yards from the Round House in Sudborough. During the 1990s it had begun to appear regularly and extended its range here so that it is now found throughout most of the old Rockingham Forest. In the current millennium Purple Emperors have been seen regularly in the Silverstone area, particularly Bucknell and Hazelborough Woods and, on one occasion, Whistley Wood. The species was recorded again in Yardley Chase from 2009 and a discovery of a caterpillar by a Northants Wildlife Trust worker confirmed its breeding there in 2011. This year also saw its return to Salcey Forest after half a century with two separate sightings.

Above: A male and female Emperor raised by 'BB' are released into 'Emperor Ride' in the mid 1980s. Photograph by Jack Steward
Right: The Round House at Sudborough, 'BB's home for a number of years, right on Fermyn's doorstep
Below: 'Emperor Ride' in Fermyn as it is today

Red Admiral *Vanessa atalanta*

Adult (wingspan 70 mm.)

Local Distribution and Status

The Red Admiral has always been the most common immigrant to our county and may be encountered almost anywhere. In the last decade it has gradually been seen earlier and earlier in the year and is certainly surviving our winters. It may well become much more common in the future than the Small Tortoiseshell and Peacock which have always hibernated here. This was certainly reflected in the 2006/2007 winter, because it was recorded on ten separate days in November, as late as December 9th, before re-appearing on 16th, 19th and 20th January, 17th February, and seven days in March when it was feeding on early cherry blossom. Such sightings represent a welcome extension to the butterfly season. There is every reason to suspect that this trend will continue and there is little to threaten the growing status of this butterfly in Northamptonshire as its caterpillar foodplant is found throughout the whole range of habitats.

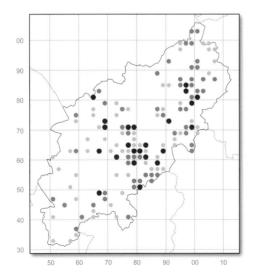

Many people who are unfamiliar with our butterflies sometimes wrongly assign the name 'Red Admiral' to any large colourful species which they see. It is such a regular visitor to most gardens each year that it is often difficult to remember that it is in fact an immigrant species. Indeed, as our winters are becoming milder, it has begun to hibernate here and can now be regarded a resident. It does not go into as deep winter inactivity as the Peacock, Comma and Small Tortoiseshell and during 2006/2007 it was recorded in every month of the year. It will also breed continuously if conditions are favourable and a caterpillar was found on 7th April 2007. Fluctuations in annual numbers have never been documented as thoroughly as those of the Clouded Yellow or even the Painted Lady. Huge numbers built up in 2006 after a hot July and during the autumn big congregations were noted around Ivy blossom. On 27th September 103 were counted round Ravensthorpe Reservoir. This followed a relatively low immigration in 2005.

The usual time for the first influx of the Red Admiral from the continent is from mid-May to early June. The butterfly should not be mistaken for any other. The wings are blackish-brown, the forewings with a red band across the middle, the tips edged in blue and broken by a series of white spots. The hindwings have a red band along the bottom edge. The underside of the hindwing is very attractive, a complex, mottled pattern of brown, bronze and blue with a creamy smudge in the centre of the top margin. Variation is rare though there is often a white spot on the red band of the forewing. Both sexes are similar in appearance.

The Red Admiral finds Ivy blossom irresistible

The butterfly will visit a range of flowers but it is interesting to note it switch from one favourite to another as the late summer unfolds. Once the garden Buddleias come into bloom it will travel some distance and desert most other flowers to probe into the purple spikes for long periods throughout the day. Occasionally it will rest on a fence or hedge and can be approached very closely as it cleans its proboscis, stroking it with its legs. As the Buddleia flowers come to an end, the smell of overripe fruit becomes a more powerful attraction. Windfall apples, cherries, plums, even blackberries and elderberries, will draw the Red Admiral It is worth placing some apples under the Buddleia to keep this butterfly in the garden.

As summer merges into autumn a show of Michaelmas Daisies or Chrysanthemums will always have a few butterflies if the weather remains reasonable but the Red Admirals cannot resist the lure of the Ivy blossom when this comes into flower in late September and October. A large clump in a sunny position will usually have some and churchyards are an important habitat. Formerly there would have been a return migration to the continent at the end of the season but the species is now able to survive the winter here and it is worth keeping an eye open for on any mild sunny day when it may appear.

Life Cycle

The Red Admiral will occur in almost any habitat, commonly breeding in woodlands and hedgerows and even river banks. Nettles in sunny positions with flourishing tender green leaves are chosen for egg-laying and the female flutters quickly over these to lay eggs in the growing tips. The egg is very small, with ten prominent grassy keels, and is laid on the upper surface of the leaf. The caterpillar will construct a shelter by first using silk to draw together the leaf where it hatched. It will create further tents by drawing several leaves together for the remainder of its life. Two colour forms are known, a black one with yellow spines and markings along the side or a light yellow form with similar markings. The final tent becomes the home of the chrysalis, which remains hidden within for about two and a half weeks. Some caterpillars succumb to parasites and a mass resembling cotton wool develops from which tiny wasps emerge.

An egg laid on the tip of a Stinging Nettle

The paler colour form of the caterpillar

The chrysalis is formed inside a shelter on the foodplant

A Red Admiral will feed for long periods on rotting fruit

An over-wintered Red Admiral on spring blossom

	Jan	Feb	Mar	Apr	May	Jun	Jul	Aug	Sep	Oct	Nov	Dec
Egg												
Caterpillar												
Chrysalis												
Butterfly												

Painted Lady *Vanessa cardui*

Adult (wingspan 65 mm.)

Local Distribution and Status

This is a regular migrant species subject to large annual fluctuations. 2009 saw a huge influx of butterflies in late May, estimated to be the largest immigration ever into the UK, but poor August weather curtailed breeding so it failed to eclipse the record year of 1996. 2010 and 2011 saw few sightings. With climate change, we may see an upsurge in Painted Lady immigrations in the future but this butterfly will never survive our winters as it makes no attempt to seek out proper hibernation sites and any real frost kills all stages. This is not surprising for a species which migrates from Africa each year.

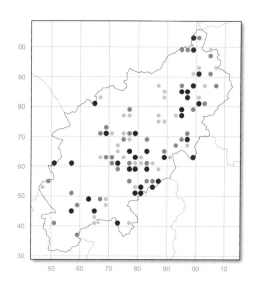

The Painted Lady is an immigrant to the British Isles which will breed successfully here provided the summer does not have a prolonged cold or wet spell. Unlike the Comma and Small Tortoiseshell which always hibernate successfully as adult butterflies and the Red Admiral, which recent research suggests is doing so on a regular basis, the Painted Lady has no hibernating stage. In consequence the scale of its appearance each year in our county can never be predicted. Usually the species is seen in ones and twos and is generally less common than the Red Admiral which can cope with adverse weather. The beginning of August is usually the optimum time for its appearance here, either from the dispersal of the offspring of spring immigrants to the south of England or the arrival of fresh migrations from the continent. Occasionally the species does arrive very early, as in 1985, when large numbers appeared at the end of April.

The Painted Lady is a distinctive butterfly. The ground colour when fresh is a lovely salmon pink which fades to a dull orange as individual butterflies age. It is adorned with a striking array of black markings and the tips of the forewings are black with white spots. There is considerable variation in the size of adults. They are fast fliers and very mobile, though the second generation which has usually bred here appears to be more sedentary and more likely to keep to the area of its birth. The underside of the butterfly is described by the famous naturalist writer 'BB' in his book *The Idle Countryman* as 'most exquisite, for they are patterned by greenish eyes and whorls, like some rich marble'. Indeed, he was so moved by witnessing the emergence of a Painted Lady from its chrysalis that he could not bring himself to kill it for his collection, which had been his intention.

Life Cycle

The species can be seen anywhere where nectar plants abound, on thistles and Ragwort on waste ground, on Knapweed and Fleabane in woodland rides and a wide variety of flowers, particularly Buddleia, in parks and gardens. Its arrival each year is eagerly awaited by the butterfly watcher who in some years is disappointed but it cannot survive our winters so is not likely to become a resident species, though it readily breeds here when it does appear. It can fly in dull weather and often late into the evening.

Such is the normal scale of the butterfly's arrival that the early stages are not usually seen. However, it can be quite easy to locate them on thistles during years of abundance. The small green egg, which appears glassy because of its sixteen prominent keels, is laid singly on the upper surface of a leaf, though sometimes several may be found on one plant. Spear Thistle is preferred but other thistles and Stinging Nettle are often used. The egg hatches within a week and the caterpillar takes up residence on the underside of a leaf, spinning a pad of silk. Here it feeds and its presence is betrayed by a silvery patch on the outside of the leaf. As it grows older, it continues to construct tents of leaves spun together, which are easily noticed because of the masses of droppings. It can be distinguished from the caterpillar of the Peacock and Small Tortoiseshell by a series of yellow lines along its side when fully grown,

The chrysalis hangs from a pad of silk and although grey in colour, it is marked with brown and shining metallic gold spots which glint in the light to resemble drops of dew, a camouflage technique. The whole life cycle can be completed within a month in favourable conditions. In 1996, after the arrival of masses of immigrants at the beginning of June, the next generation was on the wing by 20th July.

Ian Flinders' survey for Northamptonshire (1976-81) illustrates the typical pattern for this butterfly. He describes it as rare in 1978, common in 1976 and 1980 and abundant in the autumn of 1980. Similar large fluctuations occurred during the 1990s. 1993 saw only a handful of single sightings in our county. It was widely reported in 1994, while in 1995 there was an influx at the beginning of August with only scattered records for the rest of the year. Nothing can compare with the abundance of this butterfly during 1996. At the beginning of June there was a huge immigration of Painted Ladies throughout Britain, with around two hundred being seen at Farthinghoe Reserve in Northamptonshire on June 6th. They were described as 'flying in clouds, courting, mating and egg-laying in the late afternoon.' Reports flooded in from elsewhere and for the next two weeks the species was to be found almost everywhere and egg-laying was frequently observed, particularly in woodland rides. By the end of July weather conditions had remained favourable enough for these to produce another, even more numerous generation. Garden Buddleias and patches of Knapweed and thistles were alive with these lovely insects which far outnumbered our native Peacocks and Small Tortoiseshells. A subsequent count at Farthinghoe in early August recorded 350 Painted Ladies and 50-100 on a single Buddleia was a common sight.

The caterpillar can be found quite easily in good invasion years

The underside can blend perfectly with the surroundings

Part of the large invasion of 2009

Scabious is a favourite nectar plant of this species

	Jan	Feb	Mar	Apr	May	Jun	Jul	Aug	Sep	Oct	Nov	Dec
Egg												
Caterpillar												
Chrysalis												
Butterfly												

Small Tortoiseshell *Aglais urticae*

Adult (wingspan 56mm.)

Local Distribution and Status

The Small Tortoiseshell can still be regarded as a relatively widespread butterfly in our county and as a wider countryside species its habitat is not seriously threatened. A decade ago, it was one of the most common species in the county, particularly around gardens but, though still recorded over a wide area, its numbers have dwindled to a fraction of their former volume. The parasitoid *Sturmia bella*, a recent arrival from the continent, has contributed but may not be the only cause of the decline.

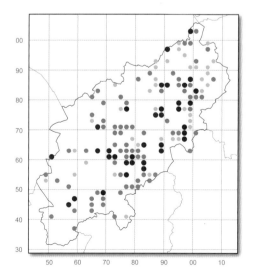

Until recently the Small Tortoiseshell was the most common Nymphalid butterfly seen in gardens and has always been very widespread in a variety of habitats. Since it breeds on Stinging Nettles and needs to feed profusely to build up its reserves to over-winter as an adult butterfly, it can be seen nectaring on a wide variety of garden flowers, especially in late summer. Buddleias can attract butterflies from miles around and late in the season Sedum and Michaelmas Daisies are particular favourites. In wilder areas, a patch of thistles will provide a valuable nectar source.

This is one of our most beautiful butterflies. Both sexes are identical. The ground colour may vary, but is usually reddish-orange with patches of black, white and yellow. The margins of both forewings and hindwings have a pretty row of blue lunules. The underside is mainly blackish-brown with areas of paler markings, making for good camouflage when egg-laying and during hibernation. In the past it may have been confused with the larger, similarly marked Large Tortoiseshell which could be encountered frequently in Northamptonshire but the latter is now considered to be extinct in Britain.

Adult Small Tortoiseshells may be observed in hibernation on the ceilings of bedrooms or in garden sheds. From here a warm spell will bring them out as early as February. Their daily activities are well documented and can easily be observed with a little patience. The morning is spent feeding and basking. Males then begin to establish territories after midday. They fly up at any intruding butterfly, driving off other male Small Tortoiseshells. When a female appears on the scene she will be pursued with vigour. In late afternoon pairs can be frequently seen with the male climbing onto the open wings of the female and touching them with his antennae. This has been observed happening repeatedly, the pair flying up and settling again every few yards. The finale occurs as the late afternoon sun is disappearing. The female suddenly dives into the nettles or other plants and settles out of view. The male follows within a few seconds and careful searching may reveal them, the pair mating side by side in their overnight roost.

Small Tortoiseshells feed on a wide range of flowers

Life Cycle

While warm weather persists the female can be found egg-laying on the underside of a young, tender nettle leaf, usually towards the edge of a large bed in a sunny, sheltered spot. The process takes place very deliberately with around eighty eggs being laid in a large batch. Two separate females have been observed laying eggs simultaneously on either side of the same leaf. As the tiny caterpillars hatch, they spin a dense web of silk over the growing leaf tips. They are conspicuous as they grow larger and strip the nettles of their leaves, moving from one plant to another. In the final stages, they separate and bask openly on the nettles. Though the caterpillars are poisonous and protected by black spines, ichneumon wasps and tachinid flies can cause heavy predation. Generally the chrysalis is difficult to find, though it has been recorded on a pale wooden fence where it was beautifully camouflaged.

Unlike the Peacock, the Small Tortoiseshell has two broods and even three in a prolonged hot summer. Tattered, over-wintered adults can still be found on the wing in June when their sparkling fresh offspring emerge. Butterflies that hatch by early August will reproduce again. Otherwise, they will feed on nectar until well into the autumn, building up their reserves to survive the winter. In cool, damp years numbers can be dramatically diminished. During 2006 and 2007, examples of chrysalides were found in bird hides in Pitsford Reservoir, with small holes in the side from which predators had emerged. A parasitoid *Sturnia bella* arrived from the continent at this time. The butterfly has been seen in much lower numbers in recent years and it remains to be seen whether this is a short-term feature or part of a long-term decline. The Small Tortoiseshell has shown the capacity to survive such fluctuations in the population in the past and the ability to recover quickly.

Egg-laying on the underside of a nettle leaf

Newly-laid egg batch

Large nest of fully-grown catrpillars

Chrysalis showing the wing pattern prior to emergence

The cryptic pattern on the underside of the butterfly's wings

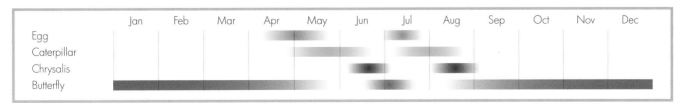

	Jan	Feb	Mar	Apr	May	Jun	Jul	Aug	Sep	Oct	Nov	Dec
Egg												
Caterpillar												
Chrysalis												
Butterfly												

Peacock *Aglais io*

Adult (wingspan 63mm.)

The Peacock is a most striking and distinctive butterfly. Its large blue 'eyes', on a reddish brown background are reminiscent of the eyes of a peacock's tail feathers, thus giving the species its popular name. It is a common visitor to gardens in spring and high summer and therefore a favourite butterfly of many people. Both sexes are similar and variation is very rare in the wild although 'blind' Peacocks can be bred in captivity.

The Peacock has a number of camouflage devices. Its underwings, in sharp contrast to the upper side, are almost black providing the illusion of a shadow when the species is at rest and making it difficult to detect when perched or settled on the ground. Should it be discovered, by a bird for instance, the butterfly will flash open its wings to produce a surprise glimpse of the large eyes which may deter the hungry predator. Individuals may be seen in which the 'eyes' have been attacked and pecked away by a bird. Another method employed by the butterfly is to rub its wings together to produce a loud rustling noise by vibration. This is called stridulation and must provide a powerful defence against small mammals. Perhaps the largest danger to the butterfly is posed by the domestic cat, which will playfully flick away individuals preoccupied with taking nectar from a Buddleia and kill them indiscriminately.

This is one of our native species which hibernates as an adult. It will spend the winter in the company of other Peacocks inside a shed, a hole in a tree or old railway tunnel. Houses are not often chosen though a local nature writer recounts how one spent the winter ensconced behind a school bell remaining undisturbed by its regular ringing and apparently only discovered when it made its rustling noise presumably in response to the vibrations. Cool church interiors are popular hibernation sites and Peacocks may be seen fluttering around a window as the warmth rises during Sunday service. Occasional warm winter days will bring out the Peacock and it has been recorded quite regularly in February in our county. It is often the first species seen in the year. These winter survivors will remain on the wing to the end of May and a few into June, by which time their colours are very faded.

Local Distribution and Status

Parasitoid wasps may take their toll of this species in some years, leading to a noticeable reduction in numbers. Conditions in the spring affect breeding success. Damp, cool weather may hinder courtship and egg-laying but promote rich nettle growth which favours the Peacock. In 1992 it was thought that numbers into the eastern counties were swelled by immigration from the continent though this is very much a common resident and there is little to suggest that it should not remain so.

The undersides of the Peacock's wings are almost black

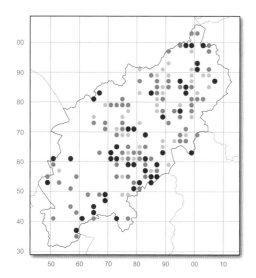

Life Cycle

Pairing has not been observed, in contrast to the Small Tortoiseshell, but butterflies are often seen to spiral upwards towards the treetops where this must take place. A larger bed of nettles than those chosen by the Small Tortoiseshell is preferred for laying eggs and these must be in a sheltered, sunny position. In common with this species it lays a large batch of eggs in an untidy cluster. The caterpillars are also very similar at first glance as they spend their first days in a web of silk, forming a large black mass. They will raise their heads en masse at any disturbance. They are usually darker than the webs of Small Tortoiseshell caterpillars with black spines as they become older. As they disperse into smaller groups in their final stage, the reddish brown legs are a distinctive feature. The chrysalis can vary in colour from darkish brown to a lighter greenish-yellow depending on the pupation site. The life cycle takes longer to complete than that of the Small Tortoiseshell so there is only one brood during the year.

The newly emerged butterfly is much more sparkling in appearance than its parents and quickly becomes numerous in late July and early August. Its sudden appearance in large numbers on the Buddleia quickly brightens up the garden. It is often the commonest butterfly in a woodland ride at this time of year found on clumps of thistles. Though purple flowers seem to be favoured, it will feed on almost any available nectar source. An individual will often be seen on the ground, wings closed. After an intense period of feeding, the Peacock will disappear as quickly as it came onto the scene, going into its long winter sleep as early as late August or the beginning of September. This gives rise to the cry, "Where have all the Peacocks suddenly gone?" Warm, sunny days in autumn bring them out for a short period and it is often the last species recorded in the year.

The caterpillar web is easily spotted in a nettle bed

The long spines can act as a deterrent against predators

Logs and tree stumps are often used for basking

Chrysalides almost ready for hatching

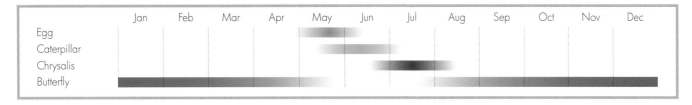

Comma *Polygonia c-album*

Adult (wingspan 55mm.)

Local Distribution and Status

Today observers can expect to see this attractive butterfly in any of the woodlands in Northamptonshire and in areas where there are a few trees or a hedgerow providing shelter. It is very numerous only after a warm spring. It is seen in gardens on Buddleias, but not to the extent of the other, more common Nymphalids, being a more likely visitor if there is a Bramble patch in a corner, a fruit tree, where the windfalls are left on the ground, or a clump of Ivy in a sunny position. Because its foodplants are common and there is plenty of suitable habitat the species is not under threat at this time and has extended its range nationally as far north as Scotland in recent years.

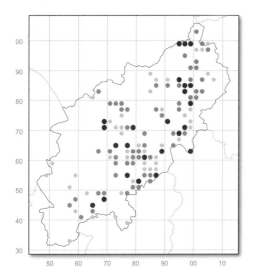

The photogenic quality of the Comma, both in its upper and undersides, can be readily confirmed by the members of Beds and Northants Butterfly Conservation since this species has repeatedly been judged the winner in our annual photographic competitions. It is quite unlike any other butterfly when seen closely as the outside of the wings is ragged in appearance. In flight it can be mistaken for a Fritillary as it flies rapidly round the head of an observer, often towards the canopy, but it usually settles a short distance away for identification to be confirmed. Both sexes are dark orange with dark brown markings though the smaller male's outline is more ragged. The underside is a beautiful mottled mixture of tan, brown and grey with green speckles, more pronounced in the male, which is lighter. A small, white marking in the centre of the hindwing, resembling the punctuation mark, gives the Comma its name.

The underside closely imitates a dead leaf both in shape and colour, a device which enables the species to hibernate in the open, unlike its cousins, the Peacock and Small Tortoiseshell, which find shelter inside. Consequently it usually, though not always, wakes from its winter sleep a little later, at the beginning of April. A warm spell as early as February can bring it out. There is a first brood of Commas from the beginning of July, in years of poor spring weather overlapping with survivors from hibernation.

The earliest adults of the first brood are a much lighter, brighter orange form, known as *hutchinsoni*. These are the ones resulting from pupation occurring before the summer solstice when day length starts to decrease. These provide the breeding stock for a second generation in August and September. Later specimens of the first brood, the normal darker form, will have gone into hibernation by this time completing a range of mechanisms to ensure survival of the species whatever the vagaries of the English weather. Occasional very dark specimens, aberration *suffusa*, have occurred in recent years in the north of the county.

The white marking on the wing from which this butterfly takes its name

The Comma is a territorial butterfly and there are little corners in most woods where it appears regularly year after year. Often it will surprise the observer as it basks, wings held flat, on a Bramble leaf. It may also be seen on the ground, taking up moisture from a woodland path or imbibing from animal droppings, notably those of horses. Flowers, such as Bramble, thistles, Fleabane and Ragwort are regular nectar sources, and it is a frequent visitor to Buddleia and Ivy blossom in gardens. However, it is in the warm, still, sunny days of September and early October that the Comma comes into its own. Windfall apples in an orchard will attract a few but overripe blackberries in a sheltered hedgerow or woodland ride will often draw several together to stock up food for the long winter sleep.

Life Cycle

At all the other stages of its life cycle the Comma exhibits the different features of camouflage. The egg is laid on the extreme tip of a tender leaf of a nettle or elm, which is also used as a foodplant in our area. It is glassy green and tiny but a female briefly and daintily alighting on a chosen leaf may be seen in the act of laying eggs. Camouflage continues in the caterpillar stage, particularly in its later life, the light tan colouring being broken by white on the top of the rear half. This helps to break up the outline of the caterpillar, resisting detection, and the resemblance to a bird dropping gives added protection. The chrysalis, which can be seen fairly easily in the wild, looks like a withered leaf and it has beautiful golden or silver markings which are reminiscent of early morning dew drops.

In the early days of the last century, the Comma was something of a rarity in our part of the country. *The Victoria County History for Northamptonshire* refers to its abundance in favourable seasons in certain West Midland and some Welsh counties. It was felt necessary to give a list of localities for the species. The writer had collected it near Oundle, and it had also been captured near Waddenham, Towcester, Yardley Chase, Sywell Wood, Lilford, Barnwell Wold and Northampton. By 1954, it was 'common in the Northampton district.', but is described as 'occasional' at Castor Hanglands in 1964. Ian Flinders survey of 1976-81 gave its status as 'frequent … and widespread throughout the county', having recorded it in 18 10 km grid squares.

The caterpillar from a distance mimics a bird dropping

The chrysalis hangs from a nettle stem

Six Commas feast on salts from fresh fox faeces

The hutchinsoni form of the Comma

A stunning aberration suffusa seen in Fermyn Woods in July 2011

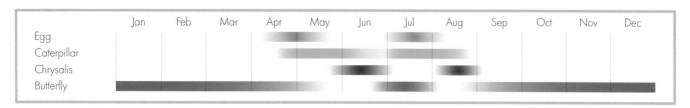

	Jan	Feb	Mar	Apr	May	Jun	Jul	Aug	Sep	Oct	Nov	Dec
Egg												
Caterpillar												
Chrysalis												
Butterfly												

Silver-washed Fritillary *Argynnis paphia*

The male has four black lines called sex-brands on each forewing (wingspan 72mm.)

Local Distribution and Status

In 2006 this butterfly made an unexpected but welcome return after two decades' absence, being recorded from six distinct localities in the county, part of a natural expansion into eastern England at the time. A couple of poor summers followed but it was seen again in six locations in 2009, 14 tetrads (2km. x 2km. squares) in 2010 and at least 16 widely distributed locations in 2011. In most of these, sightings were of one or two butterflies only. On 24th July 2010 36 were seen in Wakerley Wood with courtship and mating witnessed. Good numbers here and at nearby Fineshade Wood in 2011 confirm its return as a breeding species.

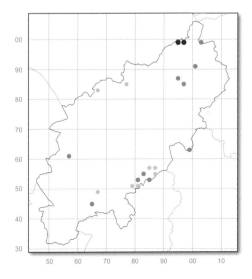

The Silver-washed Fritillary is the largest and arguably the most beautiful of the British species of Fritillary butterflies, most of which once graced the Northamptonshire countryside. It is currently the only one likely to be found in our county where it made a reappearance in 2006 after an absence of nearly two decades.

A butterfly of wide, open rides of deciduous woodland, the Silver-washed Fritillary has a rapid flight. *Hutchinsoni* Commas are similar in colour and this can lead to misidentification but this species is much larger and has a stronger, more rapid, gliding flight, often towards canopy level. It has a fondness for Bramble blossom and, when it is feeding, its beautiful markings can be examined more closely. There are two rows of large black dots inside the edge of the forewings on a light orange background. Males are distinguished by four thick black ridges along the veins of the forewing, which are scent glands, while the females have more extensive black markings on a slightly darker background. The undersides have the appearance of having been given a watercolour wash of silver and green giving rise to the butterfly's popular name. Individuals soon develop a tattered appearance as their wings catch on Bramble briars. Occasionally the species can be found on Buddleia bushes well away from its woodland haunts, as occurred in Daventry in 2006.

Life Cycle

The Silver-washed Fritillary lays its eggs on the north-facing sides of tree trunks in the vicinity of clumps of violets. The planting of conifers and the abandonment of coppicing led to its disappearance from Northamptonshire in the late 1950s/early 1960s. It requires fairly open woodland and although it will survive longer than the other Fritillaries as the rides become more shaded, it cannot breed in rough, sheltered grassland as the violets disappear.

The butterfly's flight period extends from late June to well into August, with most Northants records in mid to late July. Females are less obvious than males and when laying eggs, they flutter slowly through the trees to deposit them on tree trunks 1-15 m. up, having first investigated for the presence of violets nearby. Most often these are Common Dog-violets. The caterpillar eats the eggshell before hibernating on the tree trunk until the following spring when it descends to find violets on which to feed. Pupation takes place in early June, a few metres off the ground. The chrysalis is suspended beneath a leaf or twig and resembles a curled-up dead leaf with silvery patches.

The Victoria County History describes the Silver-washed Fritillary as 'often abundant in Salcey Forest, Whittlebury Forest and other wooded parts of the county.' Half a century later, *The Oundle School Natural History Society Journals* confirmed that it was widespread and common in the Oundle area in woods with Bramble and it was particularly abundant in the hot summer of 1947. It was still present in the Northampton district (which included Salcey and the south Northants woodlands) in 1954, but recorders at that time were commenting on an increasing scarcity of Fritillary butterflies in the woodlands of Northamptonshire, as well as Eastern England as a whole. Ian Flinders' survey of 1976-81 assigned to the species the status of 'vagrant to Northamptonshire', with only three records during the recording period. Records in Salcey Forest, subsequent to this in the early 1980s, were from known releases, and the last record until recently was from Bucknell Wood in 1989.

The first records after this occurred in 2006. The species was seen mainly in woodlands in the north of the county, i.e. Fermyn Woods, Wakerley and Fineshade and it is here where numbers have built to levels that indicate that breeding colonies have become established. In successive years it has been found in Glapthorn Cow Pastures, most of the woods of Yardley Chase, Salcey Forest, Bucknell and Hazelborough Woods, thereby returning to most of its historic range. This has possibly been triggered by climate change and has brought the butterfly back into most of eastern England. To enable the species to consolidate this trend suitable woodland habitat needs to be increased. The current change in forest management, restoring broad-leafed deciduous woodland by clearing of conifers, should assist the process.

Open woodlands are helping this butterfly to flourish in our county again

Mating pair seen in Wakerley Wood in 2010

The female is identified by her duller appearance and spots instead of stripes

The green underside acts as camouflage when roosting

	Jan	Feb	Mar	Apr	May	Jun	Jul	Aug	Sep	Oct	Nov	Dec
Egg												
Caterpillar												
Chrysalis												
Butterfly												

Speckled Wood *Pararge aegeria*

Adult in typical territorial pose (wingspan 50mm.)

Local Distribution and Status

At present, the species is common and widespread in Northamptonshire. It can be found across a range of habitats such as parkland, hedgerows and country lanes and byways. In woodland it is often the most common species encountered during the year and on dull days may be one of the few which are active. In recent years it has spread into a far wider variety of habitats and it has been recorded in an increasing number of gardens in the county, particularly in Northampton.

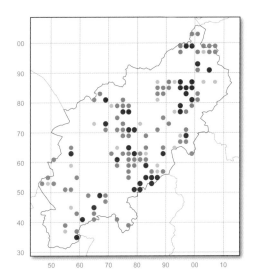

The Speckled Wood is one butterfly species whose fortunes have shown an upward trend in recent years. Like many traditional woodland butterflies, it showed a decline nationally in the second half of the nineteenth century when coppicing was abandoned. By the 1920s it had a limited distribution, being restricted to south-west England, Wales, Wiltshire, Dorset and west Sussex. However it was described as common in the Northampton district in 1954 although Flinders' survey of 1976-81 recorded it as being far more common in the south than the north of Northamptonshire.

The male Speckled Wood can often be found in a woodland glade, where there is dappled sunlight, defending its chosen sunspot which can be a protruding spray of leaves, a small Bramble or other shrub or even a patch on the ground. It will fly up at any invading butterfly, whatever the species, and chase it off before returning to its favoured perch. Humans walking through the woods may well first become aware of its presence by invading its small territory and disturbing it, and wind-blown leaves will have the same effect. A female Speckled Wood will be readily courted and mated. She may adopt a curious pose of lying on her side, wings closed, taking on the appearance of a dead leaf. Unlike its cousins, the Gatekeeper, Meadow Brown and Ringlet, the Speckled Wood will not often be seen feeding from flowers, preferring to take honeydew from its abode in the woodland canopy. It is often seen on Ivy blossom in autumn.

This is the earliest of our Brown butterflies to appear in the year, emerging as early as the end of March in an advanced spring, though more usually towards the end of April. It cannot be mistaken for any other at close quarters, the brown background being covered with cream blotches. Males have pointed wings while those of the larger female are more rounded. This is the only species which can hibernate as either a caterpillar or a chrysalis. The first butterflies to appear in the spring are those from the chrysalides and have a lighter, larger array of yellow markings, no doubt allowing them to regulate body temperature more efficiently when the canopy is more open. These will breed to provide a second generation which merges with butterflies which have now developed from the over-wintering caterpillars. A second brood from these is flying in late August to September thus providing an almost continuous supply of Speckled Woods even into the autumn. Egg-laying has been observed late into October.

Male on Bluebell in Finedon old cemetery

Life Cycle

The round, creamy-white egg is laid singly on a variety of grass blades, especially those of Cock's-foot, Wood False Brome and Yorkshire-fog. A warm sheltered location is generally chosen, under a shrub in the sunny woodland edge, hedgerow or side of a ride. Churchyard walls and the sides of ditches may also provide the necessary protection and shelter. Within ten days the egg will hatch and a yellowish-white caterpillar will emerge to eat the eggshell before feeding by nibbling small pieces from the sides of the grass blade. It later assumes a cryptic light green colour with darker green lines. Caterpillars feed for about a month, both at day and night, until they pupate low among the vegetation.

The Speckled Wood has a good tolerance of shade and the increased development of scrub in abandoned railway cuttings, gravel pits and quarries have benefited the butterfly. Shady corners of churchyards and mature hedgerows are other favourite haunts It can survive in a variety of woodland where there is a combination of light and shade, existing just as happily in modern conifer plantations as in mature deciduous woodland.

Most observers are certain of seeing the Speckled Wood if they venture into virtually any woodland in our county. Numbers fluctuate markedly from year to year and it fares best when there has been a good rainfall to promote the growth of the wild grasses upon which it is dependent for breeding. However it can also be encountered in any location where there are patches of dappled sunlight and sheltered clumps of grasses and tends to pop up when least expected. Its current expansion as a local species is most encouraging and at the present time there is no reason why it should not continue to be a common sight, particularly with plans to increase the amount of woodland in the East Midlands.

Egg being laid on the underside of a grass blade

The egg hatches out in just over a week after being laid

The caterpillar can be found on a variety of grasses

The beautiful green chrysalis suspended beneath a grass stalk

At rest, showing the underside markings

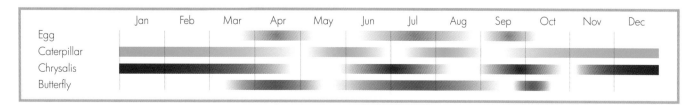

	Jan	Feb	Mar	Apr	May	Jun	Jul	Aug	Sep	Oct	Nov	Dec
Egg												
Caterpillar												
Chrysalis												
Butterfly												

Marbled White *Melanargia galathea*

Adult on Bramble (wingspan 58mm.)

Local Distribution and Status

The last decade has seen a remarkable expansion of the range of the Marbled White and it can be found throughout the county at the present time. The building of bypasses with wide grassland verges provides ideal corridors for dispersal. A colony exists by the M1 on the edge of Salcey Forest. Old quarry sites and gravel pits have also provided ideal habitat into which it was able to expand. Particularly well established colonies are at Summer Leys (first seen in 1998) and Twywell Hills and Dales (2003). The species is also thriving at Collyweston Deeps. Records came from many new localities in 2010 and 2011. The quarry area at Fermyn Woods Country Park would be ripe for colonisation but as yet there have only been occasional individuals recorded there.

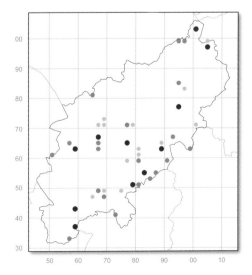

The Marbled White is not a 'White' at all, but one of our Brown butterfly species. Its distinctive wing pattern, an attractive black and white chequerboard, makes it recognisable from some distance and it cannot be mistaken for any other species. Where it occurs, on unimproved grassland, it is usually seen in large numbers at the peak of the flight period. Both sexes are very similar though the female is larger, with a more yellow tinge to the underside. The markings are more contrasting on the male, particularly on the underside. Both have the eye in the corner of each forewing which characterises our 'Brown' butterflies though it is not as evident as on the rest of the other family members.

The Marbled White has one brood each year. It usually emerges in late June or early July, peaks around the third week in July and lasts until mid-August, by which time only a few stragglers remain. It is usually numerous where a colony exists, often being seen in hundreds, and quickly becomes active in warm conditions, even under cloud. It is easily disturbed and the best times to see specimens basking with wings open are early in the morning and late in the afternoon. Its flight is quite slow compared with other species of Browns and it frequently seeks nectar from flowers. Knapweed is a particular favourite and several butterflies will congregate on one clump of blooms. Thistles, Field Scabious and Ox-eye daisies also attract it. At night, the butterfly roosts in groups among tall grasses and it is worth visiting a good site to see this in the evening as the sun is going down.

Life Cycle

The early stages are unlikely to be seen as the female is very casual, almost careless, in her egg-laying. She settles on a tall plant and shakes her abdomen until an egg appears at the tip. This is then released to fall on the ground as she flies off. The tiny caterpillar will eat the large eggshell which has no surface features, before hibernating amid dead vegetation on the ground. As the caterpillar develops it becomes nocturnal in its habits before pupating on the ground. Sheep's-fescue, Cock's-foot and Timothy are the main grasses upon which it feeds while young caterpillars are thought to need Red Fescue to survive.

In Northamptonshire, early records identify the Marbled White at Sywell Wood and Ashton Wold where it was plentiful (1856). In 1871 it was also plentiful at Barnwell Wold where a specimen was taken much later than this, in 1945. In 1937 it was 'locally common' in Oundle Wood and was abundant in the vicinity of Oundle in the late 1940s and early 1950s though there were almost none to be found there in 1959. In 1954 it was 'very local' in the Northampton district but abundant at Ashton Wold and Bedford Purlieus. Ten years later its decline was noted at Castor Hanglands where it was present in only three localities on the reserve. Fires on the heathland there, where it had been common, were cited as a possible reason for the reduction.

It may be that the abandonment of coppicing led to the Marbled White's gradual disappearance from its old woodland localities, since it likes open, sunny conditions where the fine grasses, on which it breeds, will thrive. However, this was counteracted and its survival aided by the closure of railway lines in the 1960s at a time when rabbits were in decline owing to myxomatosis.

Flinders' survey for the county (1976 – 81) records the Marbled White in eight 10km squares. At that time it favoured these railway cuttings, and single individuals outside colonies were infrequent. There were three main concentrations at this time, the abandoned railway cuttings around Brackley, Yardley Chase woodland, and Ketton Quarry just outside the county boundary. In the Brackley area, good colonies still survive in railway cuttings at Woodford Halse, Farthinghoe and the old station yard at Helmdon but use of cattle grazing at Charwelton has all but destroyed the colony there. A small population seems to have disappeared from Whistley Wood but there are occasional sightings of individuals from other woods around Silverstone. It also flies alongside the present railway line still in use near Great Brington and on the Daventry bypass. The butterfly has declined in Yardley Chase, probably because of over-zealous mowing of the rides, but it is still found in good numbers in an adjacent railway cutting just across the border in Buckinghamshire. The Ketton colony still thrives.

Present habitat conditions and favourable summers have made this butterfly a relatively common sight in Northamptonshire and the local trend is part of a recent national expansion northwards. Many of the sites mentioned above are protected nature reserves and country parks so there is every reason to be positive about its continued survival. Management of woodland to provide healthy grassland in wide rides would create another avenue for dispersal allowing it to become re-established there. Its main threat at the present time is the possible infill of its habitats as pressure on land increases and it is required for alternative uses. An example of this is the old quarry in Polwell Lane, Barton Seagrave, which held the Marbled White but was destroyed to make way for a new supermarket distribution centre.

The caterpillar becomes a nocturnal feeder in its later stages

The chrysalis can be found at the base of grass stems

Adults often bask with wings open

Scabious is a favourite nectar source

	Jan	Feb	Mar	Apr	May	Jun	Jul	Aug	Sep	Oct	Nov	Dec
Egg												
Caterpillar												
Chrysalis												
Butterfly												

Gatekeeper *Pyronia tithonus*

Female (wingspan 47mm.)

Local Distribution and Status

This species has always been very common. Ian Flinders described it as 'abundant' in Northamptonshire from 1976-81 and it remains common and widespread in the county today. Indeed, it can be found almost anywhere during its flight period. The fact that it can be numerous in such a wide range of habitats, its ability to breed within woodlands and the protected status of many sites like the country parks and the nature reserves, make its continued survival assured at the present time.

Otherwise known as the Hedge Brown, the Gatekeeper is very much a butterfly of the hedgerow and can often be seen basking or nectaring near to gates and field entrances. Its preferred habitat is tall, wild grasses beneath sunny, sheltered shrubs and it can be encountered in woodland rides, along roadside verges and on scrubby ground or the county's quarries and gravel pits rather than in more open grassland. It frequently visits gardens. Numbers are often large and it is usually plentiful in all these types of habitat in most years and particularly abundant in a dry, hot summer.

Large numbers can be seen around Bramble blossom

The Gatekeeper is only likely to be confused with the Meadow Brown but it usually has two white pupils on the eyespot on each forewing and the Meadow Brown only one. The tiny spots on the underside of the Gatekeeper's hind wings are white while those on the latter are black. When freshly emerged the male Gatekeeper is a bright orange with a brown border to the upper sides and a large sex-brand on each forewing. The female has a paler orange ground colour and lacks the sex-brand. After a short period on the wing, the butterflies soon become lighter in colour and have a 'washed-out' appearance. Aberrant specimens do occur, with extra spots along the edges of the wing, as well as the normal eyespot.

Gatekeepers usually emerge during the first few days of July and the species is single-brooded, lasting throughout August, with a very few sometimes into September though they are then very ragged. This flight period is rather more contracted than that of the Meadow Brown which flies a fortnight before and after it. The peak is at the end of July and early August. The butterflies bask with their wings fully open early and late in the day. They quickly close them during the midday heat when seeking nectar. Favourite sources of this are Bramble, Ragwort, Marjoram and Fleabane. Only flat, open flowers are used since the species has a rather short proboscis for feeding.

Life Cycle

Eggs are laid singly on grasses, often at the bases of shrubs. Tall plants of Couch, bents, fescues and meadow-grasses are chosen providing they are in sheltered spots. The butterfly either deposits eggs on leaf blades or bark or simply ejects them into the air. The eggshell is eaten on hatching and the caterpillar develops slowly over an eight-month period, hibernating among dried, curled leaves deep in the midst of a grass clump after its first skin change. It resumes feeding again in March or April. In colour it is grey-brown with darker stripes and slightly hairy. It feeds at night and is most likely to be found by shining a torch on grasses at the base of the shrub on warm evenings in May. The pretty chrysalis is formed on a leaf blade in early June beneath the same place and is very difficult to find.

Female feeding on Fleabane

The twin eye-spots can be seen on the butterfly's underside

Male, showing the very clear scent-brands

A mating pair

	Jan	Feb	Mar	Apr	May	Jun	Jul	Aug	Sep	Oct	Nov	Dec
Egg												
Caterpillar												
Chrysalis												
Butterfly												

Meadow Brown *Maniola jurtina*

Female (wingspan 55mm.)

Local Distribution and Status

The Meadow Brown has always been common and even abundant in Northamptonshire. The spraying of pesticides and ploughing of ancient meadowland have destroyed a number of colonies and local extinctions will continue to occur at the hands of ever-encroaching urban development and utilisation of sites of waste ground. However, its future is in no way threatened as there are sufficient colonies, well distributed, to enable it to quickly and effectively colonise any ground which falls from use and reverts to natural grassland.

The Meadow Brown has the reputation of being the commonest butterfly in the British Isles and is certainly to be found throughout Northamptonshire wherever there is a patch of long, ungrazed wild grassland. It is to be found in every habitat - rough meadows, hedgerows, woodland rides and edges, road verges, abandoned quarries, and railway lines and is especially abundant on unimproved meadows. It is even a visitor to gardens where they are near to breeding grounds.

When on the wing the Meadow Brown can be confused with the Ringlet, though the latter is darker and has a slower, more lilting flight. The Gatekeeper is smaller and has a dark orange appearance. The best times to see the species basking with wings open are in the early morning and late afternoon or in dull weather. The male displays only a hint of orange around a white-pupilled black eye spot near the apex of the forewings and has a black band of scent scales. The female is rather more colourful with an extensive patch of orange around the eye spots which act as a protection against attacking birds, being the object of their beaks rather than the more vulnerable body of the butterfly. Variation occurs especially in the orange colour of the female's forewings, ranging from white to brown, and in the number of pupils of the eye spot. Adults with white 'bleached' patches on one or more wings are often seen. The underside of the wings, more likely to be on view as the species rests or feeds in the sunshine, is dark brown with a paler band, the contrast being more marked on the slightly larger female.

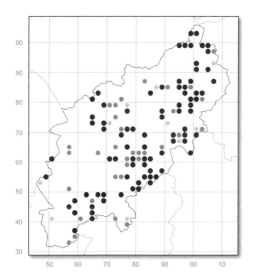

98

Life Cycle

The first Meadow Browns are usually seen in mid-June though earlier in the month in warm years. Males appear a week or ten days before the first females. Emergence is over a very long period, fresh specimens often being seen in August. The butterfly is often still around into September. Later specimens may be a partial second brood, but this is unclear. They are probably more likely part of a late emergence after periods of unfavourable weather. This being said, the Meadow Brown is perhaps the best suited to our climate of all our native species since it remains active in even the dullest weather, even in light rain, and on poor days may be the only butterfly seen. A walk through a meadow where there is a strong colony will send individuals up, flying in all directions, as they settle low in the grasses. It is very fond of flowers and frequently visits thistles and knapweeds in particular, but also a host of others, such as Ox-eye daisies and Ragwort.

Females are soon mated by the active males and may either scatter their eggs loosely on the ground or attach them to blades of grass. Favourite grasses for breeding are meadow-grasses, bents and rye-grasses. Hairy or coarse grasses are avoided. The young caterpillars are unlikely to be found, although they feed by day, because they are very tiny. They spend the winter amid grassy clumps but will emerge to feed on the grass blades on mild days. When they awake properly in the spring, they continue their feeding at night. When fully grown they are distinguishable by their white 'tails' on their green bodies, which are hairier than those of other 'Browns'. They are easily found by torchlight on warm, damp evenings in May though they are easily disturbed. The chrysalis is green with black stripes on the wing cases and is suspended from a pad of silk to a grass stem or other plant. The species spends three or four weeks in this stage.

A mating pair

The female has more orange around the eye spots on the forewings

Male, less heavily marked than the female

At roost, the eye spots on the forewing are hidden to guard against predation

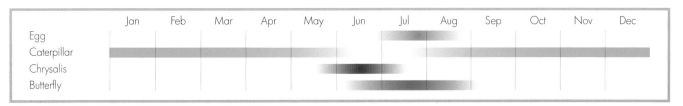

	Jan	Feb	Mar	Apr	May	Jun	Jul	Aug	Sep	Oct	Nov	Dec
Egg												
Caterpillar												
Chrysalis												
Butterfly												

Ringlet *Aphantopus hyperantus*

Female (wingspan 48 mm.)

Local Distribution and Status

Like other Brown butterflies, the Ringlet has always been common in our area. Although it is most numerous in woodland, it may also appear where there is damp grassland with some shelter and as sites become more overgrown it readily expands its range. It is less common in gardens though the odd specimen will also occur in this habitat. Its wide range of habitats and ability to breed in the damper, shadier areas of woodland and developing scrub mean that its future is not really threatened.

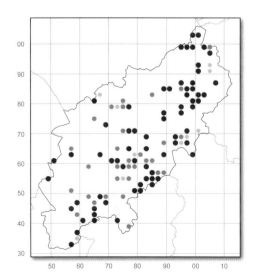

The Ringlet is a very common butterfly, especially in woodland rides and damp grasslands where hundreds may be seen at a time. It seems to prefer cool, damp, sheltered places and flies on the dullest and coolest days of July, even in light rain, when few butterflies can be found on the wing. When conditions become too cold and wet, it sinks deep into the grass stems to rest.

Ringlets are much darker butterflies than the Meadow Browns, the only similar species in our county. They have a much slower, more fluttering flight with no orange visible on the wings. When fresh, they have a clear, white fringe to the wings. Only early and late in the day, or when the temperature is low, will they bask with their wings open. Once they have warmed up they frequently nectar with their wings closed. Then the row of distinctive gold and black rings with white centres can be seen. These are larger and more numerous on the female than the male.

Aberrant specimens, with the rings much reduced in size can be found by careful searching. In July 1999 in Yardley Chase an extreme aberration was found affecting one of the hindwings only. The rings were totally absent and an almost circular white swirling line replaced them. On 27th June 2007 at Bradlaugh Fields Northampton, an example of *lanceolata* was photographed. The rings are unusually large and pear-shaped and the white pupils extended into short white streaks. On the aberration *arete*, the rings are missing with only the small eye spots remaining. This was seen in Wicken Wood in 2009 and occurs fairly regularly in Salcey Forest..

Life Cycle

Ringlets emerge in late June and fly throughout July into the first half of August though specimens soon become very worn and ragged. The peak is in mid to late July. Numbers are only reduced after an exceptional drought but soon recover in subsequent wetter years. The butterfly frequently nectars on a variety of flowers, especially brambles, thistles and Ragwort, usually with its wings closed.

Individual butterflies perch on grass heads or hover above lush tussocks of coarse grass such as Cocks-foot or Wood False Brome to drop their eggs rather than lay them. The grey, hairy caterpillars hatch after a couple of weeks, finding their foodplant readily. They enter a partial hibernation while quite small, feeding in mild weather. Searches by torchlight on warm evenings in May are the the best chance of finding them. In June a pretty, streaked chrysalis is formed at the base of a clump of grass in a small cocoon of silk.

A mating pair on Bracken

The rings on the underside which give the butterfly its name

The aberration 'lanceolata' found in Bradlaugh Fields.

The rings are missing on the forewings of this specimen

	Jan	Feb	Mar	Apr	May	Jun	Jul	Aug	Sep	Oct	Nov	Dec
Egg												
Caterpillar												
Chrysalis												
Butterfly												

Small Heath *Coenonympha pamphilus*

Adult (wingspan 36mm.)

The Small Heath is the smallest in our Brown butterflies. It is widespread though rarely found in large numbers. Counts of 10-15 are usual on most sites which consist of open grassland, green lanes, disused quarries and gravel pits and, occasionally, road verges. In all cases the turf needs to be short for the species to survive. There was a decline in numbers during the drought years of the early 1990s from which the Small Heath took a time to recover.

The butterfly is easy to distinguish amongst species of similar size. It is not as bright or golden as the three golden Skippers found locally yet is lighter and more golden than the Dingy Skipper. The upper sides of both sexes are very similar, being light orange with the characteristic eye spot in the corner of each forewing. Flight is usually low over the ground, more erratic than that of the Blues, but not as quick as the Skippers. Apart from occasional nectaring the Small Heath frequently settles on the ground, always with its wings closed. The eye spot on the forewing is shown for a time before being drawn in behind the grey hindwing, making the butterfly difficult to spot while roosting. Specimens soon become faded and worn. Often the first evidence of their presence is their flying up in front of a walker as they are disturbed from the ground.

Small Heaths fly from mid-May until well into September. There are two or sometimes three broods which overlap so that there is hardly a week in the summer when individuals cannot be found somewhere or other. Colonies are small and they seldom wander far. In fact, the Small Heath can be seen on the same small few metres of ground brood after brood, year after year.

Local Distribution and Status

In Northamptonshire the Small Heath is a butterfly of open grassland, among patches of disturbed ground such as disused quarries, the wide margins of reservoirs and lakes, abandoned railway lines and old airfields where there is plenty of bare ground and short grass to suit the species. Ian Flinders recorded it throughout Northamptonshire in his survey of 1976-81 but it has declined from a number of sites since then, particularly as disused railway lines have become overgrown and woodlands more shaded. Currently the best sites in Northamptonshire are restored gravel pits and disused quarries, such as Twywell Hills and Dales, Bradlaugh Fields, Collyweston Deeps and Old Sulehay and Ring Haw.

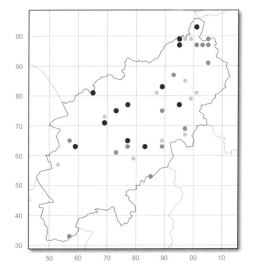

At rest on a grass head

Life Cycle

The eggs are quite large for such a small butterfly and are laid on a number of species of meadow-grasses and fescues. They hatch after a couple of weeks turning from green to whitish and freckled. The green and white striped caterpillar is beautifully camouflaged on the grass blades. It hibernates when almost full grown and pupates on grasses in early spring forming a green chrysalis with some white and black stripes. Caterpillars from the spring brood will either develop to form succeeding generations in the summer or they may hibernate until the following year in a cool summer, when the species will have only a partial second brood.

There have been many local extinctions of this butterfly where sites have become overgrown or victims of the developer. It is well distributed at the present time but is on the decline. Monitoring in the future needs to continue in order to forestall further losses from housing projects, road building and landfilling. Management of scrub is also essential on those sites where it does exist in order to maintain its long-term future. Its decline nationally has led to its designation as a UK BAP Species of conservation concern.

A mating pair, more likely to be seen in the second brood

Fleabane is a popular nectar source in late summer

Basking in the evening sunshine

Small Heaths frequently settle at ground level

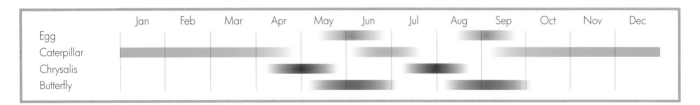

	Jan	Feb	Mar	Apr	May	Jun	Jul	Aug	Sep	Oct	Nov	Dec
Egg												
Caterpillar												
Chrysalis												
Butterfly												

Camberwell Beauty   *Nymphalis antiopa*

Sightings of the Camberwell Beauty into Northamptonshire from its home in Scandinavia have always been rare and spasmodic and it has never bred in this country. An account of 1882 lists four sightings: one taken in the grounds of the convent in Northampton 'some years ago', a second in the infirmary gardens eight years previously, a third at Wellingborough in 1872, and a fourth nearly captured by Mr Druce at Potterspury in July 1875. *The Victoria County History* tells us that, as well as these, it had also been collected near Kettering, at Thurning, and in Whittlebury Forest. In 1911 it was described as 'very scarce', with sightings at Blatherwyke and Kettering in 1893.

Three specimens were seen in Northamptonshire during the very hot summer of 1976, and there were two sightings in 1995 when an influx took place into eastern England. Given the history of the Camberwell Beauty's appearance historically, it comes as something of a surprise to note that 2006 was a record year for sightings here. Over two hundred butterflies of this species were seen then over eastern and southern England. Between 19th August and the end of the month it was seen in Old Sulehay Forest, at Earl's Barton, Newnham, Finedon, Newton Bromswold and in Fermyn Wood.

Two were seen and photographed in a garden in Brigstock feeding on greengages intermittently during the weekend of 30th August and 1st September, after which strong storms brought an all-too-sudden end to this wonderful interlude in the history of Northamptonshire butterflies.

One of the butterflies seen in a Brigstock garden in 2006
Photograph by Hilary Monk

OTHER RARE MIGRANT SPECIES

Other species have been recorded even less often. The **Swallowtail** (*Papilio machaon*) is mentioned in lists of 1882 (from Northampton) and 1907 ('near Peterborough. Larvae found many years ago'). Miriam Rothschild recorded it at Ashton Wold in 1960 and in a Polebrook garden on 1st June 1974, when it was thought to have been imported in the pupal stage in thatching reed from Hickling Broad. The **Pale Clouded Yellow** (*Colias hyale*) had occurred several times in the county according to *The Victoria County History* and in 1945 was captured at Broughton. More

recent claims of this species are likely to be *helice* Clouded Yellows. *The Victoria County History* also tells us that the **Mazarine Blue** (*Cyanaris semiargus*) had not been captured for many years, though Messrs Hull and Tomalin (1882) recorded it in Sywell Wood. A single specimen of the **Long-tailed Blue** (*Lampides boeticus*) was caught by a Northamptonshire lepidopterist in his garden on 25th July 1976. **The Queen of Spain Fritillary** (*Issoria lathonia*) had also been recorded by Hull and Tomalin upto 1882.

Above: Chequered Skipper picture taken by an Oundle School pupil in about 1958. Photograph kindly donated by Ioan Thomas.

Chequered Skipper   *Carterocephalus palaemon*

Northamptonshire was the former stronghold of the Chequered Skipper, which had a very limited range in the east Midlands until its extinction in England was declared in 1976.

In *The Victoria County History*, the species was present and sometimes abundant in certain woods about Rockingham and Kettering and at Geddington Chase, Brigstock, Whittlebury Forest, Yardley Chase and elsewhere in the county. In the Kettering area it was recorded in Weekley Hall Wood from 1917 to the 1960s. Other sites in this area were Gretton (1941), Gib Wood (1944), Hermitage Wood (1947), Bedford Purlieus (1957), Collyweston and Bangrave Wood (1958), and Cranford Wood (1966).

The Journals of the Oundle School Natural History Society recorded it in Bearshank Wood, Fineshade Wood, Bedford Purlieus, Hardwick Wood and Wakerley Wood during the period either side of the Second World War. During the hot summer of 1947 it was noticeably plentiful and providing both minor and extreme aberrations. A year later it was out early, on May 10th, but never became plentiful. A colony in Southwick Wood was almost extinct due to the disastrous shaving of the grass rides in early June 1947. In another local wood, where it had swarmed for many years, a policy of clearing grass and undergrowth in woods down to root level had had a similar effect. The best count was 38 on 31st May, where normally the species flew in hundreds. A local collector took it at Barnwell Wold in 1949 and 1950 and found it fairly common there.

The Chequered Skipper continued to be recorded until the 1960s. It was seen in Fermyn Wood and Sywell Wood in 1964, and was still common in Castor Hanglands from 1961 – 66, being on the wing from May 19th to June 12th in the last of these years. R.E.M. Pilcher wrote of this site in 1961, 'It is still very common but no longer enjoys its former abundance - an insect in no apparent danger of extinction, but well worth the trouble to maintain in good numbers.' In 1968 K.N. Bascomb tells us that it was still well established there, but none were found in the woods around Oundle, while J.H.C. Phillips failed to find it in the same year in several visits to the woods north of Kettering. In 1973 it was 'getting difficult to see' but it was still found in Castor Hanglands in 1974. The exact reasons for its extinction soon after this are unclear but changes in habitat in woodlands by the abandonment of coppicing, decline in ride management and planting of conifers are the most likely causes. Its name is commemorated on the inn sign in the village of Ashton, near Oundle.

Silver-spotted Skipper *Hesperia comma*

The Silver-spotted Skipper features on lists of butterflies in the county in 1881 and in *The Victoria County History*, and was seen at Barnwell Wold in 1882. F. O. Morris (1908) also mentions Ashton Wold as a locality. Its former range once extended as far as Yorkshire but it is never likely to have been common in Northamptonshire and is now confined to areas of short turf on downlands of southern England.

Black-veined White *Aporia crataegi*

The Black-veined White was an early extinction in the county. It features on historic lists in 1881/82 but was declared extinct in *The Victoria County History*. It formerly occurred near Peterborough, at Barnwell Wold and also on the borders of the county between Thurning and Gidding Magna in Huntingdonshire. F. O. Morris (1908) also gives Ashton Wold as a locality.

Brown Hairstreak *Thecla betulae*

The Brown Hairstreak is a difficult species to see and can easily be overlooked. *The Victoria County History* states that it was especially common in the caterpillar state in many woods, testimony to the elusive habits of the adult. Indeed, many colonies are confirmed only by egg searches during the winter, the easiest of the stages of the lifecycle to find.

In 1911, 'it was uncommon, but very local'. Barnwell Wold and Geddington Chase were known localities. It was recorded in the Kettering area at Weekley Hall Wood (1923), Hazel Beech Wood (1940), Thrapston (1947) and Helpston Heath (1956). Bedford Purlieus (1942) was another former site and it was still at Barnwell Wold in 1956. It was 'rarely seen in the Oundle area, though present' in the 1938 list in *The Oundle School Natural History Society Journal*. The same source recorded two large colonies being known to exist and probably smaller ones in other woods in 1947. Numbers of eggs were found on 4th September in that year. It was rare in the Castor Hanglands survey (1961-65) with two records only in 1961.

It is something of a mystery as to why the Brown Hairstreak has disappeared from the county while the Black Hairstreak, which shares the same foodplant, still survives but it may be that the former requires more hedgerow-type stands of Blackthorn which became shaded out with the end of coppicing regimes in the 1960s.

Silver-studded Blue *Plebeius argus*

The Silver-studded Blue formerly occurred on heathlands in the county, a suitable habitat which has long since disappeared. In 1882 it was reported from Sywell Wood and features in a list in the Oundle School Natural History Society records in 1938 when it was found on heaths but inclined to be local. It does not feature in an updated list in 1947 and its final remaining habitat may well have been ploughed up during the Second World War.

Large Blue *Phengaris arion*

The Large Blue is another species which occurred in Northamptonshire in the nineteenth century. In a list of 1882 Wigsworth and Barnwell Wold are noted as former sites. Unfortunately the species was prized greatly for its rarity and Barnwell Wold was the first British site where collectors could guarantee obtaining specimens as it was plentiful in the adjoining rough pastures. Heavy collecting took place for two decades until, during the exceptionally wet summer of 1860, 200 adults were taken at rest by one dealer and the colony never recovered. A later fire destroyed any hope of the butterfly's survival.

Duke of Burgundy photographed at Wakerley Wood in 1997

Duke of Burgundy *Hamearis lucina*

The Victoria County History tells us that the Duke of Burgundy occurred near Towcester and in Barnwell Wold and was found commonly in the woods in the county. Former sites were Fermyn Woods, Geddington Chase, Sywell Wood and Yardley Chase and it was very common in some years at Fermyn Woods and Barnwell (1911). Grafton Park Wood (1935), Bearshank Wood (up to 1947). Bedford Purlieus and Fineshade Wood were other localities. At Ashton Wold it was never abundant but present until 1935. In the Kettering area records exist for Weekley Hall Wood, where it survived for a few years from 1944, Broughton (1946), Helpston Heath (1957), Collyweston (1958) and Sywell Wood (1964).

A survey of Castor Hanglands (1962 - 65) declared that this species, once common there, had declined during this period, when the butterfly was beginning to disappear through all of its former woodland range in the country as a whole. The decline of coppicing led to the shading out of its foodplants, Cowslips and Primroses in this habitat, and it is now the most rapidly declining and threatened species in England. Ian Flinders' survey of 1976-81 failed to record it and it was declared extinct in the county. Shortly after this a colony came to light in Wakerley Wood and the butterfly was recorded here in very small numbers almost annually until the last record in 1997.

Large Tortoiseshell *Nymphalis polychloros*

The Large Tortoiseshell can be regarded as a rare migrant to Britain nowadays but is included in this section because, although never common, it would have bred in Northamptonshire in the past on woodland elms and sallows. *The Victoria County History* recorded it from Salcey Forest, Towcester, Barnwell Wold, Geddington Chase, Weekley Hall Wood and elsewhere near Kettering. In 1891 several quite fresh specimens were captured in spring, and several hibernated specimens were seen in 1902. In 1943 a specimen was observed for several days in Weekley Hall Wood.

It is thought that the Large Tortoiseshell migrated to Britain and when it did so in sufficient numbers it would breed and be seen for a few years before disappearing again. In 1947, a notable year in the history of butterfly migration, it was seen near Polebrook on the last day of the Oundle School summer term. Following breeding in 1948 there were confirmed sightings in two of the local woods in mid-April 1949, the last time such a cycle took place. It is uncertain whether more recent records of the species in this country are released specimens or rare migrants from the continent.

High Brown Fritillary *Argynnis adippe*

The High Brown Fritillary was commonly distributed throughout the woodlands at the time of *The Victoria County History* and in 1911 it was 'not uncommon'. It was described as 'local' in *The Oundle School Natural History Society Journal* in 1938. Sites included Bedford Purlieus, Weekley Hall Wood (1935), Geddington Chase (1936), Lady Wood (1939), Southwick Wood (1941), Barnwell Wold and Wakerley Wood (1942), Bearshank Wood and Helpston Heath (1943) but by 1947 it was described as 'local and scarce' in the north of the county. It was recorded in the Northampton district in 1954 but is likely to have disappeared soon after this as changes in woodland management led to the shading out of suitable habitat for violets, its caterpillar foodplant. Of all the large Fritillary butterflies this was the one most sensitive to change brought about by the abandonment of coppice cycles.

Dark Green Fritillary *Argynnis aglaja*

Like the High Brown Fritillary, the Dark Green Fritillary was once common in Northamptonshire woodlands. In the Oundle area it was found in Wakerley Wood (1937), Southwick Wood (1941) and Bearshanks Wood (1943) and was collected at Barnwell Wold (1945), while there were good numbers at Castor Hanglands in 1953. Only one appeared in this vicinity in 1949 and in 1953 it was not recorded at all, Bearshank Wood, its only haunt, having been cut down. A year later an article on butterflies of the Northampton district, which would have included Salcey Forest, Yardley Chase and the Silverstone Woods, mentions that it was still present. J.H. Payne, writing in 1965, comments on the shortage of the three large Fritillaries in the county.

Ian Flinders' survey of 1976-81 classifies it as a vagrant with only four records in the hot summer of 1976. A male was recorded in Fermyn Wood on 20th July 1983. Sightings of single specimens near the Oxfordshire border on a railway embankment at Helmdon in 1987, 1988 and 1990 gave rise for optimism of a possible re-colonisation but it has not been reported there since. Five records in the space of 18 days in 1995 suggested a small immigration into the county in that year. There were sightings from Hazelborough Forest and Fermyn Wood, an old haunt, in 1996. These were the last confirmed ones until 2009 when one was seen on Market Harborough Golf Course, just inside the county and 2010 when there were two separate sightings in Yardley Chase.

A strong colony has become established again at Sharpenhoe Clappers in neighbouring Bedfordshire and there remains a possibility that the butterfly may eventually return to some of our key grassland sites. Woodlands still remain unsuitable unless suitable coppice cycles can be re-introduced to encourage violet growth.

Pearl-bordered Fritillary   *Boloria euphrosyne*

The Pearl-bordered Fritillary was described as 'common in most of the woods' in *The Victoria County History*, and 'in most large woods' in 1911. Localities where it was originally found were Kelmarsh, Geddington Chase, Lady Wood (1940), Hardwick Wood, Fineshade Wood, Bedford Purlieus, Bullicks Wood (1955), Hazel and Thoroughsale Woods (1956). It was re-introduced to Weekley Hall Wood in 1917 and survived for the next three decades. Other sites in the Kettering records were Gretton (1939), Broughton (1942), Sywell Wood (1946), Titchmarsh Wood (1947), Helpston Heath (1949) and Wakerley Wood (1952). *The Oundle School Natural History Society Journals* give Oundle Wood as a site, and it was found in Bearshanks Wood (1943) but 1947 was not a good year and specimens were 'few and far between' in 1949. During the 1961-65 survey of Castor Hanglands there was one record only in 1962. It disappeared at about this time from the county. Yet again the destruction of suitable habitat for violet growth occurred as a result of the end of coppicing.

Small Pearl-bordered Fritillary   *Boloria selene*

The Small Pearl-bordered Fritillary was more local in the county than the Pearl-bordered even at the time of *The Victoria County History*, when it had been recorded from Waddenham and Towcester. Other sites at this time were Salcey Forest and Yardley Chase (1904), Hazelborough Forest and Bedford Purlieus (where it was still seen in 1956). In Weekley Hall Wood it was found in 1934, surviving for a decade or so. Other Kettering records are of Gib Wood (1944) and Wakerley Wood (1952). It was 'very local' in the Oundle area in 1938, but in 1947 it was not seen in that vicinity, though it was present in many localities close to Northampton. A year later 'very few' were seen near Oundle but it could still be found in the Northampton district which included most of the above sites in 1954. J.H. Payne saw one at Silverstone on June 20th 1965, the last known record. Its decline and subsequent extinction was due to reasons similar to the other members of this group

Marsh Fritillary *Euphydryas aurinia*

The Marsh Fritillary was noted under its old name of the Greasy Fritillary in a county list of 1881, a name derived from the silvery appearance which ageing specimens assume as their wing scales become worn. It was said to be found at Barnwell Wold and Polebrook, and *The Victoria County History* tells us 'it used to be found at Aldwinkle, near Waddenham, near Towcester and near Barnwell, but it appears to have disappeared for a time, as no recent specimens had been captured, e.g. it was last seen near Barnwell Wold in 1884.'

The species was to be found at Kelmarsh in the 1920s. In 1949 the Oundle School Natural History Society found a single male in a local wood where it had existed thirty years previously and another in a wood about ten miles from Oundle. There was a strong colony in the west of the county which had a high peak that year. The ground was covered with nests of caterpillars in September. A year previously a colony had been destroyed in a local wood as the result of ploughing up the site. A strong colony in the Silverstone woods survived until at least 1951. It was present in one locality in the county in 1954 but J.H. Payne, writing in 1965, comments that he saw nothing of the Marsh Fritillary that year. The butterfly must have become extinct in the county at about this time as a result of its habitat, marshy ground with a profusion of Devil's-bit Scabious, being exploited for agricultural purposes during and after the Second World War.

Glanville Fritillary *Melitaea cinxia*

The Glanville Fritillary was listed among county species in 1881 and 1882, but is absent from *The Victoria County History*. Its exact status is unclear.

Wall Browns photographed mating at Hardwick Wood in June 1991.

Wall *Lasiommata megera*

The Wall was a reasonably common butterfly in the county until the late 1980s when it could still be found frequently where the ground was disturbed in open woodland rides and old quarries, disused railway lines and airfields and even sometimes in gardens. It is a sun-loving species, and was especially common during a hot summer when numbers could build as a result of multiple broods. 1976 was an outstanding year for this species, with 200+ being recorded on 7th August.

The demise of the Wall first became apparent during the 1990s when the number of sightings diminished to a mere handful each year, with the exception of brief respites in 1995 and to a lesser extent, 1999. A couple of sightings in north Northants in 2004 were the last record of this species until 2009 (two records) and 2010 (one record on the northern edge of the county). It has disappeared from the whole of central and southern England in the last two decades for reasons which are still not understood. It can still be found around the coasts of England as far north as Northumberland and around the Irish coast but is becoming scarcer.

Grayling *Hipparchia semele*

The Grayling was recorded as occurring on Helpston Heath in 1894 (1911 list) but is not listed in *The Victoria County History*. The Oundle School Natural History Society includes it in species found in the area in 1938 and it was recorded in 1943. Suitable habitat probably disappeared as a result of the ploughing of heathland during and after the Second World War but the species was never likely to have been common here.

Large Heath *Coenonympha tullia*

The Large Heath is mentioned as occurring at Ashton Wold by Rev. F.O. Morris (1908), the only reference to this species.

The references below are included for readers to find out more about the history of Northamptonshire butterflies. Most are available in the local collection at Northampton Library:

Colston A, Gerrard C et al. Northamptonshire Red Data Book, The Wildlife Trust for Northamptonshire 1996

Izzard Martin J., The History of Butterfly Recording in Northamptonshire 1820 - 2011

Ed. Colston A & Perring F, The Nature of Northamptonshire, The Northamptonshire Wildlife Trust, Barracuda Books 1989

Morris Rev. F.O. History of British Butterflies 10th Edition 1908

Rothschild, Miriam, Entomologist's Record Vol. 87 (1975) The Swallowtail Butterfly in Northamptonshire

Ward J, Looking Back at the Butterflies and Moths of a Northamptonshire Wood (Weekley Hall Wood) - contains Kettering Natural History Society records

The Victoria County History of Northamptonshire, Vol. 1 Pages 94 - 97

Oundle School Natural History Society Journals 1937-61

The Journal of the Northamptonshire Natural History Society and Field Club:
1880 *Entomology of Northamptonshire* Hereward Wake
1882 *A Systematic Classification of the Lepidoptera which have occurred in the vicinity of Northampton* Wm Hull & H F Tomalin
1889 - 91 *Notes on the Lepidoptera of Northamptonshire* Mr W Edwards of Lilford Hall
1908 - 10 *The Lepidoptera of Northamptonshire* (1907) E. F. Wallis
1955 *Butterflies of the Northampton District* (1954) W R Spencer
1966 *Status of Butterflies on Castor Hanglands NNR 1961-65* R V Collier
1982: *The Status and Distribution of Butterflies of Northamptonshire 1976-1981* Ian Flinders

FURTHER READING

For General Butterfly Identification:
Newland D, Still R, Tomlinson D, Swash A, Britain's Butterflies, 2nd Edition Revised, WILDguides Ltd, 2010

General Reading:
Dunbar, David, British Butterflies, a History in Books, The British Library 2010.

Easterbrook, Michael, Butterflies of Britain and Ireland, A Field and Site Guide, A. & C. Black 2010

Newland, D.E., Discover Butterflies in Britain, WILDguides Ltd. 2006

Oates M, Butterflies, National Trust 2011

Quinn, Tom, BB Remembered - The Life and Times of Denys Watkins-Pitchford, Swan Hill Press 2006

Riley, Adrian M, British and Irish Butterflies, Brambleby Books 2007

Russwurm A D A, Aberrations of British Butterflies, E.W. Classey Ltd 1968

Vickery, M, Gardening for Butterflies, Butterfly Conservation 1998

For More Detailed Information on Species and Trends:
Asher J, Warren M S, Fox R, Harding P T, Jeffcoate G & S, The Millennium Atlas of Butterflies in Britain and Ireland, OUP 2001

Fox R, Asher J., Brereton T. Roy D, Warren M S, The State of Butterflies in Britain and Ireland, Butterfly Conservation, Pisces Publications 2006

Fox R & Asher J. 2010 Atlas of Butterflies in Britain and Ireland, Butterfly Conservation 2010

Heslop I R P, Hyde G E, Stockley R E, Notes and Views of the Purple Emperor, The Southern Publishing Co. Ltd. 1964

Joy J, Williams M, Jeffcoate S, Conservation of the Wood White Butterfly (Leptidea sinapis) National Sites Dossier, Butterfly Conservation Report S10-16 August 2010

Thomas J. & Lewington R, The Butterflies of Britain and Ireland, 2nd Edition Revised, British Wildlife Publishing 2010

Douglas Goddard was born in Lincolnshire and educated at Horncastle Grammar School and St John's College, York. He was Deputy Head of a Northampton school and Manager of a local branch of a supply teacher agency before retiring. He is married with a son, daughter and two granddaughters. He has recorded, photographed and studied the butterflies of Northamptonshire since 1983 and received an Outstanding Volunteer Award from Butterfly Conservation in 2011.

Andy Wyldes Northamptonshire born and bred, he has always had a passion for butterflies, spending countless hours observing and photographing them. He is currently the editor of the local branch magazine for Butterfly Conservation.

This book is dedicated to Margaret and Claire, our 'butterfly widows'.

First published in Great Britain in 2012 by Douglas Goddard & Andy Wyldes and the Bedfordshire and the Northamptonshire Branch of Butterfly Conservation

ISBN 978-0-9520291-4-4

Printed by LPPS Ltd, www.lppsltd.co.uk

Butterfly Conservation
Company limited by guarantee, registered in England (2206468)
Registered Office: Manor Yard, East Lulworth, Wareham, Dorset, BH20 5QP
Charity registered in England & Wales (254937) and in Scotland (SCO39268)